D1293051

The Discipline
of Numbers

FOUNDATIONS OF SCIENCE LIBRARY

The Natural World
(4 volumes)

The Majesty of the Heavens
(Foundations of Astronomy)

The Round World
*(Foundations of Geology and
Geomorphology)*

The Skies and the Seas
*(Foundations of Meteorology, Ocean-
ography & Cartography)*

The Ages of the Earth
*(Foundations of Palaeogeography and
Palaeontology)*

The Biological Sciences
(6 volumes)

The Life of Animals without
Backbones
(Foundations of Invertebrate Zoology)

The Life of Animals with
Backbones
(Foundations of Vertebrate Zoology)

The World of Plants
(Foundations of Botany)

Breeding and Growing
*(Foundations of Genetics, Anthropo-
logy and Agriculture)*

Patterns of Living
(Foundations of Ecology)

Human Kind
(Foundations of Human Biology)

The Physical Sciences
(9 volumes)

The Restlessness of Matter
*(Foundations of Aerodynamics, Hydro-
dynamics and Thermodynamics)*

The Science of Movement
(Foundations of Mechanics and Sound)

Lightning in Harness
(Foundations of Electricity)

The Silent Energy
(Foundations of Electrical Technology)

The Cathode Ray Revolution
(Foundations of Electronics)

The Rays of Light
(Foundations of Optics)

The Unseen Spectrum
*(Foundations of Electromagnetic
Radiation)*

The Cosmic Power
(Foundations of Nuclear Physics)

The Discipline of Numbers
(Foundations of Mathematics)

The Chemical Sciences
(4 volumes)

The Fundamental Materials
(Foundations of Basic Chemistry)

The Elements and their Order
(Foundations of Inorganic Chemistry)

The Giant Molecules
(Foundations of Organic Chemistry)

The Chemist at Work
*(Foundations of Analysis and
Laboratory Techniques)*

Technology
(5 volumes)

The Metallic Skills
(Foundations of Metallurgy)

Industrial Processing
*(Foundations of Industrial and Chemical
Technology)*

Engineering Technology
(Foundations of Applied Engineering)

Automobile Engineering
(Foundations of Car Mechanics)

The Inventive Genius
(Foundations of Scientific Inventions)

History and Reference
(3 volumes)

The Beginnings of Science
(Foundations of Scientific History)

Frontiers of Science
(Foundations of Research Methods)

A Dictionary of Scientific Terms
*(The Foundations of Science Reference
Book)*

CHIEF EDITORS

Leslie Basford, B.Sc.   Philip Kogan, M.Sc.

ASSISTANT EDITORS

Michael Dempsey, B.A., Michael Gabb, B.Sc., Clare Dover, B.Sc.
Cyril Parsons, B.Sc., Joan Pick, B.Sc., Michael Chinery, B.A.
David Larkin, B.Sc., Paul Drury Byrne, B.Sc.

CONSULTANT EDITORIAL BOARD

Sir Lawrence Bragg, M.C., O.B.E., F.R.S., M.A., Nobel Laureate
Sir James Chadwick, F.R.S., Ph.D., M.Sc., Nobel Laureate
Norman Fisher, M.A.
Sir Harry Melville, K.C.B., F.R.S., Ph.D., D.Sc.
Professor J. Z. Young, F.R.S., M.A.

The Discipline of Numbers

Foundations of Mathematics

DUDLEY SACKETT, B.Sc., B.T.

FOUNDATIONS OF SCIENCE LIBRARY

THE PHYSICAL SCIENCES

DISTRIBUTED IN THE U.S.A. BY
Ginn and Company : *BOSTON*
PUBLISHED BY
Sampson Low, Marston and Co : *LONDON*

This new presentation assembles
freshly edited material from
'Understanding Science' on one
subject into a single volume.

Copyright © 1966 Sampson Low, Marston & Co. Ltd.

Library of Congress Catalog Card
Number: 66–17981

Catalog No.: L–20710

Made and printed in Great Britain by
Purnell & Sons Ltd., Paulton
(Somerset) and London

510
S121d

109219

MATHEMATICS

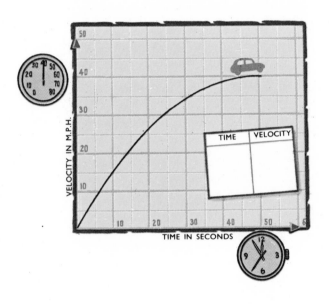

Contents

Arithmetic,
Geometry
and Algebra

CHAPTER ONE

Mathematical Rules

A ball game without rules would result in complete disorder. And, in mathematics, there have to be set rules for playing with numbers. Some of these rules are obvious and self evident. We use them unconsciously because they always give the expected answer. But the rules are important – they define the game. Mathematical rules define the number system in operation. *Real numbers* – the natural numbers, the integers, the rationals and irrationals – use the same basic rule-book. They have five properties in common. They are as follows: two commutative properties, two associative properties (both for addition and multiplication) and one distributive property which together make up the five properties of real number systems. These five basic properties do not show *how* the game is to be played – they are merely rules of order and arrangement. Other kinds of quantity – e.g. *imaginary numbers* and *vectors* – follow a different set of rules.

The operations for rational numbers are more involved than the methods for natural numbers and integers, because the rational number is really a pair of numbers. Rules for addition on the denary (scale of tens) system are different from the rules of the binary (scale of twos) system.

The four fundamental operations are addition and subtraction, multiplication and division. Two or more of these may appear on the same line. Which operation is to have priority? Operations carried out in different orders may give different results.

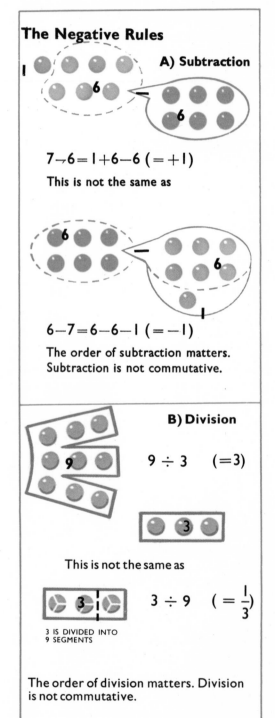

The Negative Rules

A) Subtraction

$7 - 6 = 1 + 6 - 6 \ (= +1)$

This is not the same as

$6 - 7 = 6 - 6 - 1 \ (= -1)$

The order of subtraction matters. Subtraction is not commutative.

B) Division

$9 \div 3 \quad (= 3)$

This is not the same as

$3 \div 9 \quad \left(= \frac{1}{3} \right)$

3 IS DIVIDED INTO 9 SEGMENTS

The order of division matters. Division is not commutative.

Multiplying and Dividing

Multiplying 8 × 12 is the same as adding 8 twelve times. Dividing is the same as multiplying by one-over-the-number. It is the *inverse* of multiplication. Multiplication tables vary according to the number scale in operation – binary tables are different from denary tables.

Adding and Subtracting

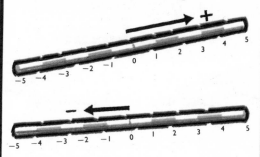

Natural Numbers and Integers

Addition and subtraction can be represented as movements along the number line, to right (addition) and to left (subtraction). This would work either for the scale of tens, or for the scale of twos.

Which is the right order?

To avoid confusion, the rule-book lays down that multiplication and division have priority over addition and subtraction, and, all other things being equal, should come first. If, however, it is essential that addition come before multiplication, the addition is enclosed in brackets. Brackets are a method of showing when the basic rule-book properties are amended. The operation inside a pair of brackets must be carried out before any others. This priority rule is included in the *distributive* property of

---

The Five properties of all real number systems

Each of these five properties looks, at first sight, obvious. Here the properties are set down first for natural numbers, then for fractions and then for the general numbers and symbols, written here as A, B and C.

Addition is Commutative

$$3 + 4 = 4 + 3$$
$$\frac{1}{3} + \frac{1}{4} = \frac{1}{4} + \frac{1}{3}$$

$$A + B = B + A$$

Multiplication is Commutative

$$3 \times 4 = 4 \times 3$$
$$\frac{1}{3} \times \frac{1}{4} = \frac{1}{4} \times \frac{1}{3}$$

$$A \times B = B \times A$$

Addition is Associative

$$3 + (4 + 5) = (3 + 4) + 5$$
$$\frac{1}{3} + \left(\frac{1}{4} + \frac{1}{5}\right) = \left(\frac{1}{3} + \frac{1}{4}\right) + \frac{1}{5}$$

$$A + (B + C) = (A + B) + C$$

Multiplication is Associative

$$3 \times (4 \times 5) = (3 \times 4) \times 5$$
$$\frac{1}{3} \times \left(\frac{1}{4} \times \frac{1}{5}\right) = \left(\frac{1}{3} \times \frac{1}{4}\right) \times \frac{1}{5}$$

$$A \times (B \times C) = (A \times B) \times C$$

Multiplication is Distributive over Addition

The Priority rule is:
Brackets
Ofs
Division
Multiplication
Addition
Subtraction

$$3 + 4 \times 5 = 3 + 20 = 23$$
$$\text{but } (3 + 4) \times 5 = 7 \times 5 = 35$$

In equations, the golden rule is 'fair play' to both sides

In other words, an operation carried out to one side (perhaps to simplify the equation) must also be done to the other side. The balance (signified by the 'equals' sign) must be preserved.

Adding numbers to both sides of an equation is like adding the same weights to both sides of a balance. Similarly, the same weights can be subtracted from both sides.

Destroying the balance by adding (or subtracting) more to one side than the other. Balanced equations produce **equivalent statements,** unbalanced equations do not.

Obeying the 'Fair Play' Rules – Dividing and Subtracting

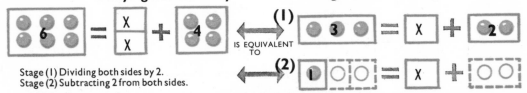

IS EQUIVALENT TO

Stage (1) Dividing both sides by 2.
Stage (2) Subtracting 2 from both sides.

$$6 = 2x + 4 \quad \Leftrightarrow \quad 3 = x + 2 \quad \Leftrightarrow \quad x = 1$$

'When the same operation is carried out on both sides of an equation, the result is an equivalent statement of the equation. The object is to isolate the unknown, x, on one side of the equation.

Obeying the 'Fair Play' Rules – Multiplying and Adding

(1)

IS EQUIVALENT TO

Stage (1) Multiplying both sides by 4.

(2), (3)

Stage (2) Adding 4 to both sides.

IS EQUIVALENT TO

Stage (3) Subtracting x from both sides.

$$1 + \frac{x}{4} = \frac{x}{2} - 1 \quad \Leftrightarrow \quad 4 + x = 2x - 4 \quad \Leftrightarrow \quad 8 + x = 2x \quad \Leftrightarrow \quad x = 8$$

Here there are unwanted fractions, and it is best to multiply first to convert them to whole numbers. Then two stages are needed to isolate x, a subtraction and an addition. These are illustrated in one.

number systems.

Is $4 + 3$ the same as $3 + 4$? Or is $4 - 3$ the same as $3 - 4$? In the first example, it is the same, and in the second it is not. When numbers are to be added, their order does not matter, and can be changed around. But numbers being subtracted cannot be changed around. Addition is said to be *commutative*; subtraction is not. In the same way, multiplication is also commutative, division is not. 3×4 equals 4×3, but $3 \div 4$ is not equal to $4 \div 3$

Is $2 + (5 + 7)$ the same as $(2 + 5) + 7$? In the first, the operation $5 + 7$ is carried out first; in the second $2 + 5$ is carried out first. Both give the result 14. So the grouping together of numbers for addition does not matter, and nor does it matter for multiplication. Again, subtraction and division are excluded. Addition and multiplication are said to be *associative*, while subtraction and division are not.

Reductio-ad-absurdum

In English if a wrong meaning is attributed to a word in a sentence or phrase it can result in reductio-ad-absurdum. The following passage will explain this point. Candlelight is brighter than nothing but nothing is brighter than light from the sun, therefore candlelight is brighter than sunlight! So in Mathematics if the rules are not rigidly adhered to the results can be equally absurd. The following is a good example of what goes wrong when the game is not played according to the rule book.

The sum of the natural numbers is

$$S = 1 + 2 + 3 + 4 + 5 + 6 \\ + 7 + 8 + \ldots\ldots\ldots\ldots\ldots$$
$$= (1 + 3 + 5 + 7 + \ldots\ldots) \\ + (2 + 4 + 6 + 8 + \ldots\ldots)$$
$$= (1 + 3 + 5 + 7 + \ldots\ldots) \\ + 2(1 + 2 + 3 + 4 + \ldots\ldots)$$
$$= (1 + 3 + 5 + 7 + \ldots\ldots) + 2S$$
$$\therefore \quad S > 2S$$

(where $>$ means 'is greater than')
$$\therefore \quad 1 > 2$$

The mistake is not so obvious here but clearly there is one, and on a closer examination it is found that the sum of the natural numbers in the second bracket is only of more or less half the total numbers in the original problem and therefore cannot equal S.

CHAPTER TWO

Number Patterns, Prime Numbers and Cancelling

NUMBERS can be arranged in certain systematic patterns. Three of these well-known pattern arrangements are: (i) rectangular, (ii) triangular and (iii) square.

Rectangular Numbers

Any number which cannot be arranged in a rectangular pattern is a *prime number*. Examples are 1, 2, 3, 5, 7, 11, 13.

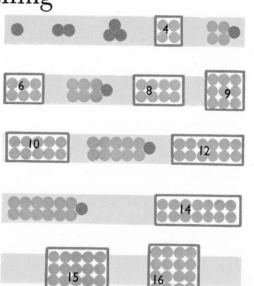

Each rectangular number is equal to the product of the rows and columns. Thus from the diagram $15 = 3$ rows $\times 5$ columns and the numbers 3 and 5 are called *factors* of 15. Most numbers can be arranged in more than one rectangular pattern and therefore have more than one set of factors. For example:

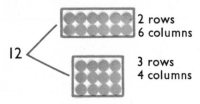

12 — 2 rows 6 columns
— 3 rows 4 columns

In every case the rows and columns can be interchanged because multiplication is commutative.

Triangular Numbers

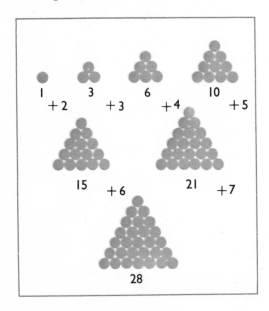

Each successive triangular number is formed by adding 1, 2, 3, 4, etc. (the gap between successive triangular numbers) to the immediately preceding number. The number added is the number in the base of the $\triangle$ and also indicates the number of rows or 'courses' in the $\triangle$.

Thus:

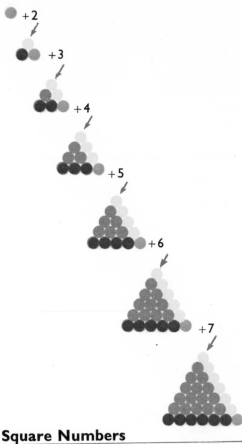

Square Numbers

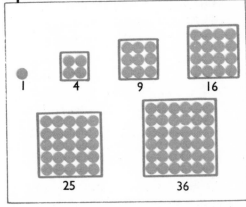

To form successive square numbers, successive odd numbers are added to each preceding number. It is easy to see why the numbers added must be successively odd because whether the rows and columns contain an odd or even number, twice an odd number is even and twice an even number is even. The corner is filled with a single number, thus making the total number added always odd. Thus we have

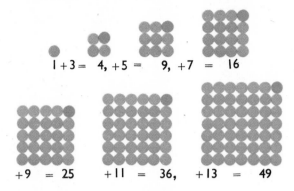

$1 + 3 = 4, +5 = 9, +7 = 16$

$+9 = 25$ $+11 = 36, +13 = 49$

Also pairs of successive triangular numbers give the square numbers. Thus:

Triangular Numbers

$0 \rightarrow 1 \rightarrow 3 \rightarrow 6 \rightarrow 10 \rightarrow 15 \rightarrow 21 \rightarrow 28$

$\downarrow \quad \downarrow \quad \downarrow \quad \downarrow \quad \downarrow \quad \downarrow \quad \downarrow$

$1 \quad 4 \quad 9 \quad 16 \quad 25 \quad 36 \quad 49$

Square Numbers

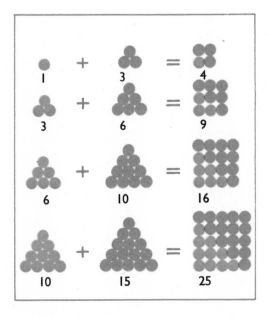

An EVEN number (except 2) can never be a prime number, because all even numbers are either *rectangular* or *square* numbers, that is they can be arranged in at least two rows, each containing the same number of units. The number of rows can be ascertained by dividing by 2, 3, 4, etc. – the natural numbers. Any number therefore exactly divisible by any of the natural numbers and giving an answer other than one cannot be *prime*.

Rules for Easy Division

A number has 3 as a factor if 3 is also a factor of the sum of the digits making up the number.

Thus 219351 has 3 as a factor because $2 + 1 + 9 + 3 + 5 + 1 = 21$, $2 + 1 = 3$ also has 3 as a factor. Or more simply $(2 + 1)(9)(3)(5 + 1)$ has 3 as a factor because the sets of numbers in the brackets each have 3 as a factor.

A number has 4 as a factor if the number is EVEN and remains EVEN after dividing by 2. For a number of more than two digits these criteria (standards of judgement) need be applied to the last two digits only. Thus 58924632 is EVEN and $\frac{32}{2} = 16$, which is also EVEN, hence 4 is a factor.

A number has 5 as a factor if it ends in 5 or 0.

A number has 6 as a factor if EVEN and divisible by 3.

A number has 9 as a factor if 9 is also a factor of the sum of the digits making up the number. Thus 7254711 has 9 as a factor because $7 + 2 + 5 + 4 + 7 + 1 + 1 = 27$, $2 + 7 = 9$ also has 9 as a factor. Or more simply $(7 + 2)(5 + 4)(7 + 1 + 1)$ has 9 as a factor because the sets of numbers in the brackets each has 9 as a factor.

A number has 11 as a factor if the difference of the sum of the ODD placed digits and the sum of the EVEN placed digits is either 0 or a number divisible by 11. Thus 685212 has 11 as a factor because the sum of ODD placed digits, $2 + 2 + 8 = 12$, and the sum of EVEN placed digits, $1 + 5 + 6 = 12$, on subtraction gives $12 - 12 = 0$. Again 2091804 has 11 as a factor because the sum of ODD placed digits, $4 + 8 + 9 + 2 = 23$, and the sum of EVEN placed digits, $0 + 1 + 0 = 1$, on subtraction gives $23 - 1 = 22$ which is divisible by 11.

Cancelling

Sometimes a number appears in an equation as one number divided by another. For example $\dfrac{6}{3}$. This number is obviously equal to 2. The point is that when one or both of the numbers can be split up into factors, they may be found to have a factor in common (a common factor). $\dfrac{6}{3} = \dfrac{3 \times 2}{3}$

3 is common to both the top and the bottom. When this happens, it is possible to divide both top and bottom of the fraction by the same factor (cancel out the common factor, leaving only 2). This is done automatically for a very simple problem like 6-over-3. Cancelling is useful when the numbers involved are cumbersome. It is a way of simplifying.

Example

It is not easy to see that 2 × 243 × 88 × 143 divided by 121 × 39 × 81 × 16 is unity (one). Laborious multiplication will prove this to be so. But the method of successive cancelling is an easier and better approach to the problem. This particular question also highlights the advantage *division* has over *multiplication*. Multiplication results in *bigger* numbers whereas division results in *smaller* numbers. A main aim in mathematics is to make numbers smaller not bigger. So always *divide* rather than *multiply* when faced with the choice.

$$\frac{2}{121} \times \frac{243}{39} \times \frac{88}{81} \times \frac{143}{16} = 1$$

When cancelling through a number use a faint horizontal line so that the original number can still be seen clearly under it. The new number should be written above the old one observing the correct placing of the digits (units, tens etc.)

CHAPTER THREE

The Number Line

1, 2, 3, 4, 5, and so on are called the *natural numbers*. They are far from being the only kind of number. There is no such thing as a negative natural number. This raises difficulties when subtracting natural numbers. To understand exactly what subtraction involves, it is best to deal in another kind of number system, the *directed numbers*, or *integers*.

This can be seen by plotting the numbers so that they are evenly spaced along a line, the *number line*. The centre of the number line is zero, or the

$$L_{10} \; L_9 \; L_8 \; L_7 \; L_6 \; L_5 \; L_4 \; L_3 \; L_2 \; L_1 \quad O \quad R_1 \; R_2 \; R_3 \; R_4 \; R_5 \; R_6 \; R_7 \; R_8 \; R_9 \; R_{10} \; R_{11}$$

The integers are arranged on the number line, positive integers to the right and negative integers to the left.

MBERS TO THE LEFT ON
E NUMBER LINE ARE
UIVALENT TO NEGATIVE
MBERS

NUMBERS TO THE RIGHT
ON THE NUMBER LINE ARE
EQUIVALENT TO POSITIVE
NUMBERS

origin. It is marked 0. All the numbers marked on the line to the right of 0 are written R_1, R_2, R_3, etc. The numbers to the left are written L_1, L_2, L_3, and so on. Adding three units means starting at 0 and going three units along the R direction (the positive direction) to arrive at R_3. It is like going up in a lift from the ground floor to the third floor. After this, the instruction may be to go down two floors. On the number line, this instruction is move along L_2 units. It is equivalent to going two steps back along the number line to arrive at R_1. Another instruction to move along L_1 units means arriving back at the origin again. Written mathematically this last step is

$$R_1 + L_1 = 0$$

R_1 is, of course, what we normally write as $+1$, and L_1 is equivalent to -1. Therefore $L_1 = -R_1$, $L_2 = -R_2$ etc.

In most books, no distinction is made between the directed numbers and the natural numbers. But there is a difference, and, although eventually it is correct to write 1, 2, 3, etc. for R_1, R_2, R_3, etc. and -1, -2, -3, etc. for L_1, L_2, L_3, etc., it is better to stay with the R and L notation until subtraction is completely understood.

One of the first difficulties in

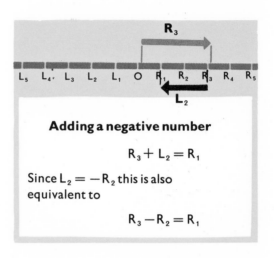

Adding a negative number

$$R_3 + L_2 = R_1$$

Since $L_2 = -R_2$ this is also equivalent to

$$R_3 - R_2 = R_1$$

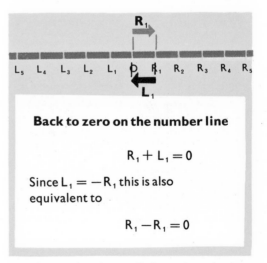

Back to zero on the number line

$$R_1 + L_1 = 0$$

Since $L_1 = -R_1$ this is also equivalent to

$$R_1 - R_1 = 0$$

mathematics is realizing that 'minus a minus equals a plus'. This can be illustrated by an amusing anecdote thus: A zoo was raided by thieves who found that selling camels to the Arabs was a profitable business and decided to relieve the zoo of two of its inmates. The thieves managed to get the camels away but in the struggle that ensued the camels lost their tails. In the morning when the zoo-keeper came on duty he found the camels missing but the two tails were there in evidence of the felony that had been perpetrated. Mathematically this is: Zoo minus two camels, the camels being minus two tails

Zoo − (2 camels − 2 tails)

Zoo − 2 camels + 2 tails

thus showing that minus a minus equals a plus.

In mathematical symbols the problem of $R_3 - (-R_2)$ can be stated as follows: Since $L_2 = -R_2$ the problem can be stated as $R_3 - L_2$ which is the same as $R_3 + (-L_2)$ and since $-L_2 = +R_2$ the final way of writing the problem is $R_3 + R_2 = R_5$. In other words, in subtracting negative numbers the direction on the number line is reversed twice, and after two reversals is left pointing in the positive direction.

This rule of arithmetic works for all directed numbers (or *integers*). So whenever a negative integer is to be subtracted, the process can automatically be turned into addition.

$$R_3 \qquad -L_2 = +R_2$$

$$L_9 \; L_8 \; L_7 \; L_6 \; L_5 \; L_4 \; L_3 \; L_2 \; L_1 \quad O \quad R_1 \; R_2 \; R_3 \; R_4 \; R_5 \; R_6 \; R_7 \; R_8 \; R_9$$

Subtracting a negative number is equivalent to adding the same positive number.

$$R_3 - L_2 = R_3 + (-L_2)$$
$$\text{but} \qquad L_2 = -R_2$$
$$\therefore \qquad -L_2 = +R_2$$
$$\therefore \quad R_3 - L_2 = R_3 + R_2 = R_5$$

Minus a Minus Equals a Plus

The tank is slowly being emptied, and it is filmed with a cine camera. Emptying the tank is equivalent to subtraction; filling it is equivalent to addition. The film can be played back either forwards (positive) or backwards (negative). When it is played backwards, the tank appears to be filling. Subtracting a negative quantity is equivalent to addition.

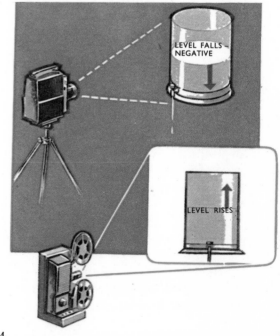

LEVEL FALLS — NEGATIVE

LEVEL RISES —

CHAPTER FOUR

Number Systems

NUMBER systems are purely arbitrary. The system in use and adopted by convention and general practice is the decimal or *denary* system. This system was probably the result of the human race being born with ten digits on two hands. But other systems are beginning to become useful, and, who knows, they may eventually replace the existing system entirely or be used as alternative systems. Already the binary system which uses only two digits, 0 and 1, is a system of the greatest importance and is the basis of digital computers which today are revolutionising the performance of complex calculations. Three other systems are worth discussing as an exercise in recapturing some of the difficulties we must have experienced as children and had to overcome to become proficient in using the present system in our everyday calculations.

Ancient man used to think in *fives* because he had five fingers on his hand (the clumsy Roman system is also based, among other things, on fives).

If we ignore the thumb on each hand this reduces the digits on both hands to EIGHT and this could easily have formed a basis for a number system.

Again the number TWELVE has so many associations for us that it may easily have been an advantage as a basis of a number system. There are 12 units in a dozen, 12 dozen in a gross, 12 inches in a foot, 12 months in a year and one could go on for a long time like this. Besides, 12 is a factor of many numbers which again have useful associations. Take sixty, for instance. There are sixty minutes in an hour, sixty seconds in a minute, sixty minutes in a degree and so on.

The Denary or TEN System

Our number system is based on counting in tens. There are ten digits, from 0 to 9. After this come the number of tens, and the number of tens of tens (hundreds). 31 is equal to three tens and one unit. 648 is equal to six hundreds plus four tens plus eight units.

$31 = 3$ tens $+ 1$ unit.

$648 = 6$ hundreds $+ 4$ tens $+ 8$ units. The 'tens' scale is called the *denary* scale.

When adding in the denary scale, the units are added together first, then the tens, then the hundreds, and so on. When the number of units comes to 10 or more, extra tens are carried on to the tens column. When the number of tens is 10 or more, extra hundreds are carried on to the hundreds column.

The FIVE System

There is no digit five in a system based on five. Neither are there the digits 6, 7, 8, 9. 5 in this system is written as 10, and 6 as 11. Counting in five goes:

1, 2, 3, 4, 10, 11, 12, 13, 14, 20 . . . 21 in the 'fives' system does not stand for the same number as 21 in the denary system. 21 in 'fives' corresponds to 11 in 'tens'.

The Binary or TWO System

No one now uses the fives system, but a great many modern electronic computers think in a 'twos' system.

DENARY	1	2	3	4	5	6	7	8	9	10	11	12	13	14	15	16
SCALE OF FIVES	1	2	3	4	10	11	12	13	14	20	21	22	23	24	30	31
BINARY	1	10	11	100	101	110	111	1000	1001	1010	1011	1100	1101	1110	1111	10000

This is called the *binary* system. There are no symbols 2, 3, 4, 5, 6, 7, 8 or 9. 2 becomes 10. 3 becomes 11. 4 becomes 100, and so on. In fact, all numbers are represented on the binary scale by just two digits, 1 and 0.

Denary: 1 2 3 4 5 6 7 8
Binary: 1 10 11 100 101 110 111 1000.

There is a straightforward way of converting any denary number into a binary number. The denary number is successively divided by 2. The remainder (which can be either 1 or 0) forms part of the binary number.

For example, 7 divided by 2 is 3-remainder-1. The first digit of the binary number (starting from the right) is therefore 1. To find the second digit, 3 is divided by 2. The result is 1-remainder-1. The second digit is 1, and the third digit must also be 1, for there is only a 1 remaining. This method works for all numbers, no matter how large. If an even number i.e. divisible by 2) appears at any stage, the remainder is 0, and a 0 digit

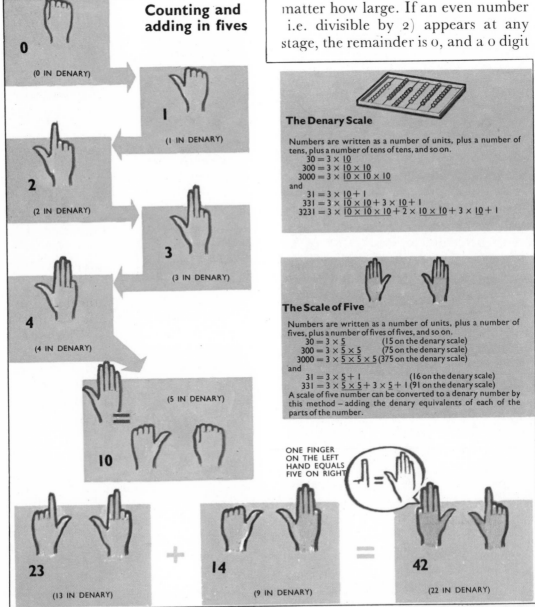

Counting and adding in fives

0 (0 IN DENARY)

1 (1 IN DENARY)

2 (2 IN DENARY)

3 (3 IN DENARY)

4 (4 IN DENARY)

5 (5 IN DENARY)

10

The Denary Scale

Numbers are written as a number of units, plus a number of tens, plus a number of tens of tens, and so on.
$30 = 3 \times \underline{10}$
$300 = 3 \times \underline{10 \times 10}$
$3000 = 3 \times \underline{10 \times 10 \times 10}$
and
$31 = 3 \times \underline{10} + 1$
$331 = 3 \times \underline{10 \times 10} + 3 \times \underline{10} + 1$
$3231 = 3 \times \underline{10 \times 10 \times 10} + 2 \times \underline{10 \times 10} + 3 \times \underline{10} + 1$

The Scale of Five

Numbers are written as a number of units, plus a number of fives, plus a number of fives of fives, and so on.
$30 = 3 \times \underline{5}$ (15 on the denary scale)
$300 = 3 \times \underline{5 \times 5}$ (75 on the denary scale)
$3000 = 3 \times \underline{5 \times 5 \times 5}$ (375 on the denary scale)
and
$31 = 3 \times \underline{5} + 1$ (16 on the denary scale)
$331 = 3 \times \underline{5 \times 5} + 3 \times \underline{5} + 1$ (91 on the denary scale)
A scale of five number can be converted to a denary number by this method – adding the denary equivalents of each of the parts of the number.

ONE FINGER ON THE LEFT HAND EQUALS FIVE ON RIGHT

23 (13 IN DENARY) + 14 (9 IN DENARY) = 42 (22 IN DENARY)

17	18	19	20	21	22	23	24	25	26	27	28	29	30
32	33	34	40	41	42	43	44	100	101	102	103	104	110
10001	10010	10011	10100	10101	10110	10111	11000	11001	11010	11011	11100	11101	11110

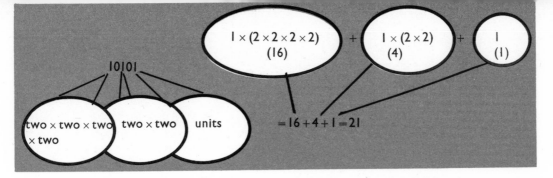

$$1 \times (2 \times 2 \times 2 \times 2) \quad + \quad 1 \times (2 \times 2) \quad + \quad 1$$
$$(16) \qquad\qquad (4) \qquad (1)$$

10101

two × two × two × two   two × two   units

$$= 16 + 4 + 1 = 21$$

BINARY ADDITION

$$\begin{array}{r} 1010(10) \\ + 1011(11) \\ \hline 10101(21) \end{array}$$

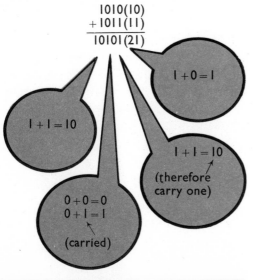

1 + 0 = 1

1 + 1 = 10

1 + 1 = 10
(therefore carry one)

0 + 0 = 0
0 + 1 = 1
(carried)

CHECK IN DENARIES
1010 = 10 denary
1011 = 11 denary
10 + 11 = 21 denary
21 denary = 10101

BINARY SUBTRACTION

$$\begin{array}{r} 10101(21) \\ - 1010(10) \\ \hline 1011(11) \end{array}$$

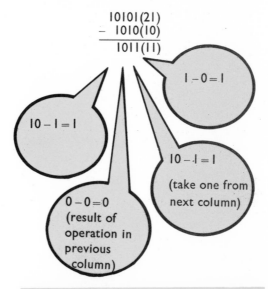

1 − 0 = 1

10 − 1 = 1

10 − 1 = 1
(take one from next column)

0 − 0 = 0
(result of operation in previous column)

CHECK IN DENARIES
10101 = 21 denary
1010 = 10 denary
21 − 10 = 11 denary
11 denary = 1011

The Binary Scale

BINARY			10		11		00	
DENARY	(0)	(1)	(2)		(3)		(4)	

Numbers are written as a number of units, plus a number of twos, plus a number of twos of twos, and so on starting from the right.

$10 \longleftrightarrow 1 \times 2$ (2 on the denary scale)
$100 \longleftrightarrow 1 \times 2 \times 2$ (4 on the denary scale)
$1000 \longleftrightarrow 1 \times 2 \times 2 \times 2$
$\qquad\qquad\qquad$ (8 on the denary scale)

and

$111 \longleftrightarrow 1 \times 2 \times 2 + 1 \times 2 + 1$
$\qquad\qquad\qquad$ (7 on the denary scale)
$1010 \longleftrightarrow 1 \times 2 \times 2 \times 2 + 1 \times 2$
$\qquad\qquad\qquad$ (10 on the denary scale)

A binary scale number can be converted to a denary number by splitting it up, like this, into units, twos, twos of twos, and so on, and then adding up the total in denary scale numbers.

Converting from Denary to Binary

The method involves dividing one denary number repeatedly by two. The remainders form the binary number. The denary number 42 is taken as an example.

		remainder
2)42,	21 groups of 2	0
2)21,	10 groups of 2×2	,, 1
2)10,	5 groups of $2 \times 2 \times 2$	,, 0
2)5,	2 groups of $2 \times 2 \times 2 \times 2$	,, 1
2)2,	1 group of $2 \times 2 \times 2 \times 2 \times 2$	,, 0
1		1

So the binary equivalent of 42 is 101010

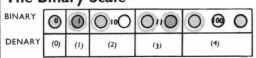

31	32	33	34	35	36	37	38	39	40	41	42	43
111	112	113	114	120	121	122	123	124	130	131	132	133
111	100000	100001	100010	100011	100100	100101	100110	100111	101000	101001	101010	101011

is inserted in the binary number.

The binary system is particularly useful because the 0 and 1 can stand for ON and OFF in an electrical circuit. Digital binary computers are really complicated switching networks, capable of two positions, either ON or OFF. It is possible to design the switches so that the computer can add and subtract – in fact perform all arithmetical processes. Though there are many more digits in a binary number to add and subtract, each separate addition is simpler, because the answer can only be either 1 or 0.

Denary:

$$17$$
$$49+$$
$$\overline{66}$$

Binary:

$$10001$$
$$110001+$$
$$\overline{1000010}$$

It can easily be checked (by successive division by 2) that 66 in the denary system is 1000010 in the binary system.

There are only three rules to remember when adding:

$$0 + 0 = 0$$
$$1 + 0 = 1$$
$$1 + 1 = 10$$

There are similar rules for subtraction:

$$1 - 1 = 0$$
$$10 - 1 = 1$$
$$1 - 0 = 1$$

A desk calculating machine is unlikely to add in twos. Ten is a more likely scale because the numbers do not then need to be transformed into binary numbers before they are fed to the machine. The calculator is based on drums with 10 possible positions. The drums are coupled together so that, after the ninth position, the drum moves the next drum on the left on one space. This corresponds to 'carrying one' in ordinary addition on the denary scale.

The Octem or EIGHT system

If we wish to devise a system of less than ten digits out of the existing system, then no new numbers need be invented. In a system using EIGHT of these digits there would be no number eight (8) or nine (9). The 'octem' number ten will receive a new name which can be chosen arbitrarily, say SET, and a completely new terminology devised, based on the existing system. Thus in the denary scale of numbers EIGHT would correspond to SET and be written as ten (10) in the new 'octem' or EIGHT system and the counting would then go oneset, twoset, thrset, etc. Sixteen (16) in the denary system would be twensety in the octem system. The sets of EIGHT would have the names: set, twensety, thrsety, forsety, fivsety, sixsety, sevnsety and 100 in the octem scale of numbers would be, say, 'disetem'.

The Duo or TWELVE system

In this system which involves more than ten digits as a set, new digits will have to be invented. The number 12 in the denary scale would be written 10 and called *duo* in the *twelve* system. The numbers TEN (10) and ELEVEN (11) in the denary scale will have to be invented in the duo (TWELVE) scale because the 'set' is not completed until the number TWELVE (12) is reached. Let us write TEN (10) in the denary scale as NET (1·) in the duo (TWELVE) scale and ELEVEN (11) in the denary scale as VEN (1 ∧) in the duo (TWELVE) scale. Thus the count would go ONE (1), TWO (2) . . . NINE (9), NET (1·), VEN (1 ∧), DUO (10), ONE DUO (11), TWO DUO (12) . . . NINE DUO (19), NET DUO (2·) VEN DUO (2 ∧), TWO DUOTY (20) and the

	44	45	46	47	48	49	50	51	52	53	54	DENARY
	134	140	141	142	143	144	200	201	202	203	204	SCALE OF FIVES
	101100	101101	101110	101111	110000	110001	110010	110011	110100	110101	110110	BINARY

sets of TWELVE would go: duo, twoduoty, thrduoty, forduoty, fivduoty, sixduoty, sevnduoty, eightduoty, nineduoty, netduoty, venduoty, and 100 in the 'duo' or TWELVE scale of numbers would be, say, 'diduotem'. The scales with their terminology are compared here.

Scales and their Terminology

Terminology								set	oneset	twoset	thrset	forset	fivset	sixset	sevnset	twenset	twensety-one	twensety-two	twensety-three	twensety-four	twensety-five	twensety-six	twensety-seven	thrsety	forsety
OCTEM	1	2	3	4	5	6	7	10	11	12	13	14	15	16	17	20	21	22	23	24	25	26	27	30	40
DENARY	1	2	3	4	5	6	7	8	9	10	11	12	13	14	15	16	17	18	19	20	21	22	23	24	32
DUO	1	2	3	4	6	5	7	8	9	1·	1∧	10	11	12	13	14	15	16	17	18	19	2·	2∧	20	28
Terminology								net	ven	duo	oneduo	twoduo	thrduo	forduo	fivduo	sixduo	sevnduo	eightduo	nineduo	netduo	venduo	twoduoty	woduoty-eight		

Terminology	forsety-four	fivsety	sixsety	sevnsety	sevnsety-four	disetem	disetem and set	disetem and twensety	disetem and twensety-four	disetem and thrsety	disetem and forsety	disetem and forsety-four				
OCTEM	44	50	60	70	74	100	110	120	124	130	140	144				
DENARY	36	40	48	56	60	64	72	80	84	88	96	100	108	120	132	144
DUO	30	34	40	48	50	54	60	68	70	74	80	84	90	1··	11∧	100
Terminology	thrduoty	thrduoty-four	forduoty	forduoty-eight	fivduoty	fivduoty-four	sixduoty	sixduoty-eight	sevnduoty	sevnduoty-four	eightduoty	eightduoty-four	nineduoty	netduoty	venduoty	diduotem

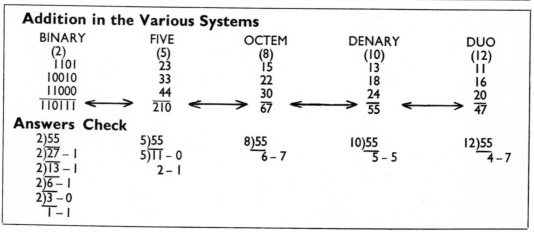

Addition in the Various Systems

BINARY (2)	FIVE (5)	OCTEM (8)	DENARY (10)	DUO (12)
1101	23	15	13	11
10010	33	22	18	16
11000	44	30	24	20
110111	210	67	55	47

Answers Check

```
2)55          5)55          8)55          10)55          12)55
2)27 – 1      5)11 – 0      6 – 7         5 – 5          4 – 7
2)13 – 1      2 – 1
2)6 – 1
2)3 – 0
1 – 1
```

19

CHAPTER FIVE
Significant Numbers

ONE of the nearest stars in the sky is some 207,000,000,000 miles away from the Earth. This does not mean that the star is exactly 207 thousand million miles away. Its distance is being quoted as a round figure, to the nearest thousand million miles.

It would certainly be unjustified to state that the star was 207,402,410,711 miles from the Earth, because measurements of stellar distances can never be made to the nearest mile. In measuring vast distances, the error can be quite considerable – a few hundred million miles either way. Another factor makes nonsense of quoting too many figures. As the Earth orbits the Sun, its distance from a star can change by 186,000,000 miles, the approximate diameter of the Earth's orbit. So it is meaningless to give the

star's distance to even the nearest million miles, unless the position of the Earth at the time is quoted as well.

To show that measurements are inexact, or that the distance fluctuates, the noughts are inserted instead of any other numbers, and the distance is given to the nearest round figure.

A 4 in a number always stands for four, and a 7 always stands for seven, but 0 does not necessarily stand for the number nought. In this example, the noughts after the 7 are fill-ins, and they show the order of magnitude of the distance. But the 0 between the 2 and the 7 obviously does not stand for the number nought. It is said to be a *significant figure*. The other noughts are *not significant*.

The significant figures in the number 0·00067 are 6 and 7. The noughts are not significant, showing only that

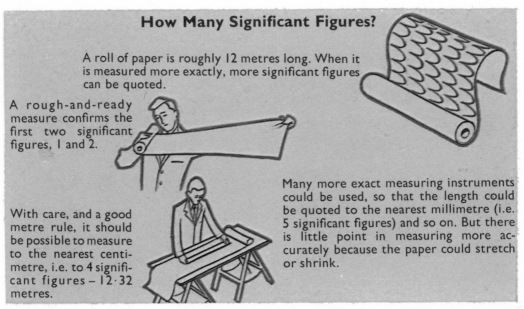

How Many Significant Figures?

A roll of paper is roughly 12 metres long. When it is measured more exactly, more significant figures can be quoted.

A rough-and-ready measure confirms the first two significant figures, 1 and 2.

With care, and a good metre rule, it should be possible to measure to the nearest centimetre, i.e. to 4 significant figures – 12·32 metres.

Many more exact measuring instruments could be used, so that the length could be quoted to the nearest millimetre (i.e. 5 significant figures) and so on. But there is little point in measuring more accurately because the paper could stretch or shrink.

the 6 means six ten-thousandths, and the 7 means seven hundred-thousandths.

The significant figures of any number are the ones which are known beyond any shadow of doubt. They are the figures which should be quoted in the results of any experiment. If length measurements are involved they should not be quoted to the nearest millimetre when the accuracy of the measuring instrument is only to the nearest centimetre. If, during the calculation stage, inaccurately-known values are multiplied and divided by each other, it is possible to end with a long string of figures by continuing the long multiplication or division longer than is necessary. Only the first few figures are significant. The number of them depends on the accuracy of the measurements.

The answer should be corrected 'to the nearest significant figure'. For example, if the answer comes to 1812,

Bathroom scales cannot measure to the nearest gram, and the weight of the human body fluctuates with the time of day. Only 2 significant figures can be quoted.

WEIGHT AFTER MEAL – 61 KILOS

WEIGHT AFTER POCKETS ARE EMPTIED – 59 KILOS

and the figure 2 cannot be justified it is written as 1810. But if the answer comes to 1817 at the end of a calculation, its value, to three significant figures, would be 1820.

CHAPTER SIX

Units

COUNTING the number of people in a room is easy. One person = one unit. When dealing with whole objects it is easy to add and subtract because one object = one unit. However, very few convenient units of length occur in nature. Units like the foot and the yard do have some form of natural basis. A foot is roughly the length of a man's foot and a yard the length of a man's stride. The foot and the yard are not very well defined by this, because different people have different sized feet and varying strides.

When making any measurement of length, area or volume, the measurement must always be made in stand-ard, well-defined units. Since there are no obvious natural units for any of these quantities, Man has devised convenient artificial standards – such as the foot and the metre.

Units of this size are useful for measuring the height of a chair, or the length of a room. But no-one would quote the diameter of a microscopic bacterium in metres – they use far smaller units, the micron, or the Ångstrom unit. These smaller units are in fact based on the metre. A micron is a millionth of a metre, and an Ångstrom unit is a ten-thousand-millionth of a metre. Small units based on the foot are never used in scientific

SOME EARLY UNITS OF MEASUREMENTS

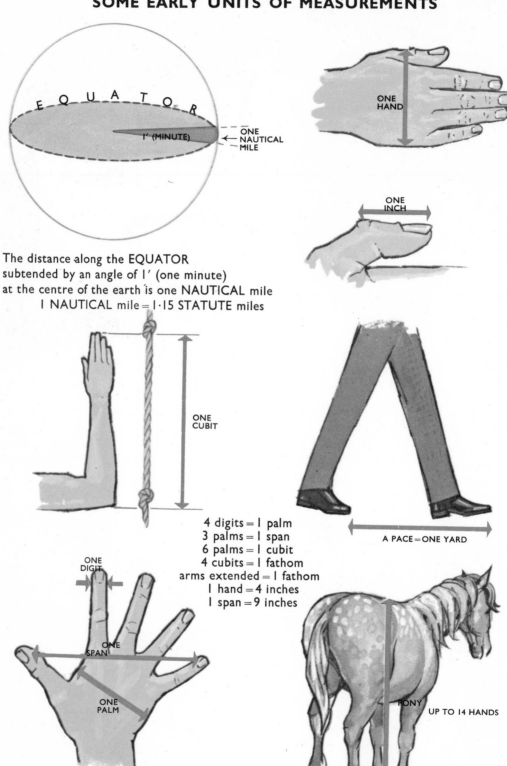

The distance along the EQUATOR
subtended by an angle of 1′ (one minute)
at the centre of the earth is one NAUTICAL mile
1 NAUTICAL mile = 1·15 STATUTE miles

EQUATOR

1′ (MINUTE)

ONE NAUTICAL MILE

ONE HAND

ONE INCH

ONE CUBIT

4 digits = 1 palm
3 palms = 1 span
6 palms = 1 cubit
4 cubits = 1 fathom
arms extended = 1 fathom
1 hand = 4 inches
1 span = 9 inches

A PACE = ONE YARD

ONE DIGIT

ONE SPAN

ONE PALM

PONY   UP TO 14 HANDS

The scientific length unit, the metre, is defined as 1,553,164·13 wavelengths of the red light emitted by a special kind of cadmium lamp. This arbitrary choice is nevertheless accurately reproducable in scientific laboratories throughout the world.

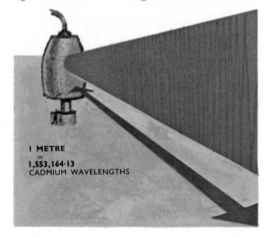

I METRE
=
1,553,164·13
CADMIUM WAVELENGTHS

work.

Larger distances are also measured in larger units – the mile, and the kilometre. Distances to stars are so vast that they are quoted in light years. This unit is based neither on the foot nor on the metre. It is the distance light can travel (at 186,000 miles per second) in a year. One light year is 5,880,000,000,000 miles.

Units of Area

An area of carpet can be measured in square feet, square yards, or, in the metric system, in square metres. The unit of area is the square, the side of which is unit length.

The area of a circle is also quoted in 'square units'. It would, of course, be possible to have as a unit the area of a circle of unit radius. But it would be very difficult to measure an area with a measuring circle. The only shape the circle would fit on to would be a circle of equal radius. Square units are easily fitted round each other.

The volume units are measurements requiring three dimensions; the unit cube of unit side is the starting point of measurements of volume. But of course not all volumes can be neatly packed into tidy little parcels of unit cubes and the difficulty arises when measuring fluids by this unit. Nobody would ask a heating engineer to estimate the electrical capacity of a storage heater required for a living room of 1,600 gallons capacity. But there is a connection, and a rough and ready basis of conversion gives

1 cubic foot $\longleftrightarrow$ 6¼ gallons (water)

Squares are better than circles as units of area.

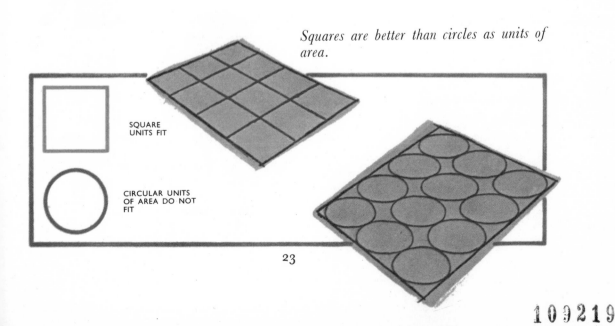

SQUARE
UNITS FIT

CIRCULAR UNITS
OF AREA DO NOT
FIT

23

109219

Length Units

Factors of 12, 3 and 1760 are involved in the British and American Systems of inches, feet and yards. 10 is the only factor needed to convert from smaller to bigger units in the metric system.

(m = metre)

1 Ångstrom unit (Å)	=	$\dfrac{1}{10,000,000,000}$ m
1 Micron (μ)	=	$\dfrac{1}{1,000,000}$ m
1 millimetre (mm)	=	$\dfrac{1}{1,000}$ m
1 centimetre (cm)	=	$\dfrac{1}{100}$ m
1 decimetre (dm)	=	$\dfrac{1}{10}$ m
1 decametre (Dm)	=	10 m
1 hectometre (Hm)	=	100 m
1 kilometre (Km)	=	1,000 m

Some other Common Units of Measurement

unit of sound – a decibel

unit of current – an ampere

unit of heat – a calorie or a therm

unit of angular distance – a degree

unit of force – a dyne

unit of work – erg or joule

unit of speed on water – a knot

unit for silk and nylon – a denier

CHAPTER SEVEN

Fractions and Decimals

SIMPLY, a fraction is:

$$\frac{\text{a Numerator number}}{\text{a Denominator number}}$$

or

$$F = \frac{N.}{D}$$

When $N < D$ ($<$ means less than) the fraction is called a *proper* fraction. When $N > D$ ($>$ means greater than) the fraction is called an *improper* fraction.

This is a division sign $\div$. If the dots are replaced by numbers we have a fraction, say $\frac{2}{7}$.

Fractions and decimals often occur in problems. Rarely is the solution a 'whole number', a *natural number*, or an *integer*. The rules for manipulating fractions and decimals are different from the rules for natural numbers and integers.

$$F = \frac{N}{D}$$

N < D
Proper Fraction

N > D
Improper Fraction

24

Adding Fractions and Decimals

Add $\frac{1}{3}$ to $\frac{1}{3}$ and the answer is $\frac{2}{3}$. This can easily be seen by doing the addition along a number line. To add these two fractions, the rule is to add the top half of each fraction to get the top half of the total (the *numerator*) but leave the lower parts, the *denominators*, alone.

This particular addition is made easy because both fractions belong to the same set of fractions:

$$\{\tfrac{1}{3}, \tfrac{2}{3}, \tfrac{3}{3}, \tfrac{4}{3}, \ldots\}$$

Another way of writing this set of numbers is as *ordered pairs* of numbers. $\frac{1}{3}$ is written as the *ordered pair* (1,3). All fractions can be written as ordered pairs, the numerator first, the denominator second. So the above set becomes:

$$\{(1,3), (2,3), (3,3), (4,3), \ldots\}$$

The rule for adding ordered pairs is: leave the second number of the pairs alone, but add the first ones. This produces exactly the same result as adding the number pairs in their fraction form.

But this method does not work for fractions like $\frac{1}{4}$ and $\frac{1}{3}$. $\frac{1}{4}$ can be written as the ordered pair (1,4) and $\frac{1}{3}$ as the ordered pair (1,3). Ordered pairs with 4 as their second number belong to a different set from pairs with 3 as their second number. Rules for adding ordered pairs apply only when both the numbers to be added *belong to the same set*. The total then *belongs to the same set*.

It is possible to get round this difficulty by writing (1,4) as (3,12) and (1,3) as (4,12). (3,12) and (4,12) both belong to the same set. This works for simple fractions, but not for more complicated ones. It is better to convert the fraction or ordered pair to a *decimal fraction*. $\frac{1}{3}$ in decimals is $0\cdot\dot{3}$ (nought-point-three-recurring). If all the numbers are written as decimals, they all belong to the same set, and it is possible to add them easily. The total also belongs to the set of decimal fractions.

Multiplying and Dividing

Decimals are best for adding and subtracting when the fractions do not

Adding Fractions

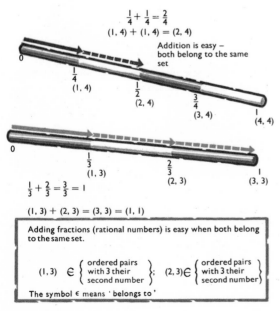

$$\tfrac{1}{4} + \tfrac{1}{4} = \tfrac{2}{4}$$
$$(1, 4) + (1, 4) = (2, 4)$$

Addition is easy – both belong to the same set

$$\tfrac{1}{3} + \tfrac{2}{3} = \tfrac{3}{3} = 1$$
$$(1, 3) + (2, 3) = (3, 3) = (1, 1)$$

Adding fractions (rational numbers) is easy when both belong to the same set.

$(1,3)$ $\in$ $\left\{\begin{array}{l}\text{ordered pairs}\\\text{with 3 their}\\\text{second number}\end{array}\right\}$; $(2,3) \in \left\{\begin{array}{l}\text{ordered pairs}\\\text{with 3 their}\\\text{second number}\end{array}\right\}$

The symbol $\in$ means 'belongs to'

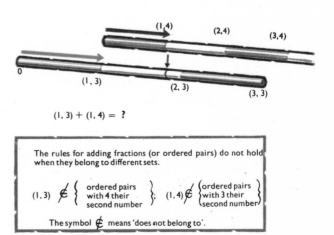

$$(1, 3) + (1, 4) = ?$$

The rules for adding fractions (or ordered pairs) do not hold when they belong to different sets.

$(1,3)$ $\notin$ $\left\{\begin{array}{l}\text{ordered pairs}\\\text{with 4 their}\\\text{second number}\end{array}\right\}$; $(1,4) \notin \left\{\begin{array}{l}\text{ordered pairs}\\\text{with 3 their}\\\text{second number}\end{array}\right\}$

The symbol $\notin$ means 'does not belong to'.

25

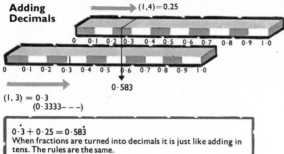

Adding Decimals

(1,4) = 0.25

0 0·1 0·2 0·3 0·4 0·5 0·6 0·7 0·8 0·9 1·0

0 0·1 0·2 0·3 0·4 0·5 0·6 0·7 0·8 0·9 1·0

0·583

(1, 3) = 0·$\dot{3}$
(0·3333– – –)

0·$\dot{3}$ + 0·25 = 0·58$\dot{3}$
When fractions are turned into decimals it is just like adding in tens. The rules are the same.

belong to the same set. Multiplication and division are, however, best carried out with fractions. No-one would think of multiplying $\frac{1}{4}$ by $\frac{1}{3}$ by turning them into their decimal form 0·25 and 0·$\dot{3}$, because it would involve a cumbersome long multiplication.

The answer to any fractional multiplication can be seen by putting two number lines at right angles. If $\frac{1}{4}$ is to be multiplied by $\frac{1}{3}$, $\frac{1}{4}$ is marked along one number line and $\frac{1}{3}$ along the other. $\frac{1}{4} \times \frac{1}{3}$ is the area of the rectangle bounded by the marked-off parts of the number line. This rectangle is a twelfth of the unit area.

If, instead, $\frac{3}{4}$ is marked off along one number line, and $\frac{2}{3}$ along the other, the marked-off area is $\frac{6}{12}$, the unit area. The rule for multiplication is: multiply the two numerators together and the two denominators together to get the final fraction. The rule works for any number of fractions multiplied together. The fraction $\frac{6}{12}$ can then be cancelled to its simplest form, $\frac{1}{2}$. In practice the simplification by cancelling is done prior to the multiplication.

If the fractions are written as ordered pairs [for example (3,4) and (2,3)] the rule is very similar. Multiply the first parts of the pairs together, and the second parts of the pairs together, to give the first and second

Multiplying fractions

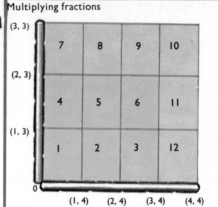

The unit markings on the number lines enclose unit area. The area enclosed by (2, 3) and (3, 4) is equal to the product of (2, 3) and (3, 4). The third and quarter markings on the number line divide the unit area into twelfths. The (2, 3) and (3, 4) markings enclose 6 of the twelfths, so:

$$\frac{2}{3} \times \frac{3}{4} = \frac{6}{12} = \frac{1}{2}$$

$$(2, 3) \times (3, 4) = (6, 12) = (1, 2)$$

$$2 \times 3 \quad 3 \times 4$$

The rule for multiplying ordered pairs – multiply the first numbers of the pairs, then the second numbers of the pairs. This rule applies even when the fractions do not belong to the same set of ordered pairs.

Dividing fractions

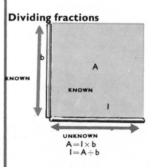

Division is the inverse of multiplication. It is like starting off knowing an area and one side, and then finding the other side.

UNKNOWN
$A = 1 \times b$
$1 = A \div b$

For example: $\frac{1}{2} \div \frac{1}{3}$

or (1,2) ÷ (1,3) writing it in ordered pairs.

The rule in fractions is: Turn the divisor $\frac{1}{3}$ upside down

$\frac{1}{2} \times \frac{3}{1}$

and multiply. $\frac{1}{2} \times \frac{3}{1} = \frac{3}{2} = 1\frac{1}{2}$.

The rule in ordered pairs is: Multiply first number by second and second by first.

Note that $\frac{1}{3} \div \frac{1}{2}$ is *not* the same as $\frac{1}{2} \div \frac{1}{3}$

parts of the resulting ordered pair. This rule works for the entire set of rational numbers (numbers which can be written as ordered pairs).

Division is also best done in fractions. It is the *inverse* of multiplication.

We have seen that $\frac{1}{4} \times \frac{1}{3} = \frac{1}{12}$ and therefore $\frac{1}{4} \div \frac{1}{3}$ cannot equal $\frac{1}{12}$ if we are to agree that multiplication and division are opposite in character. This means that if the operation of multiplication by a number were to be performed in a mathematical calculation and then a division carried out involving the same number, the result would be equivalent to a return to normal or back to square one in common parlance. For example

$$6 \times 2 = 12; \quad 12 \div 2 = 6,$$

that is $6 \times 2 \div 2$ gives 6 again and therefore dividing by 2 is equivalent to multiplying by $\frac{1}{2}$.

Also $\quad \frac{1}{4} \div \frac{1}{3} \times \frac{1}{3} = \frac{1}{4}$

Multiplying both sides of the equation by $\frac{3}{1}$ we have

$$\frac{1}{4} \div \frac{1}{3} \times \frac{1}{3} \times \frac{3}{1} = \frac{1}{4} \times \frac{3}{1}$$

$$\therefore \quad \frac{1}{4} \div \frac{1}{3} = \frac{3}{4}$$

this is $\longleftrightarrow \frac{1}{4} \div \frac{1}{3} = \frac{1}{4} \times \frac{3}{1} = \frac{3}{4}$.

So, when dividing by a fraction the rule is to turn the *divisor* upside down, and then multiply as ordinary fractions. If the fractions are in the form of ordered pairs [for example (1,12) and (1,3)], then the rule is: multiply the first number of the first pair by the second number of the second pair. Then multiply the second number of the first pair by the first of the second. This gives the final ordered pair

$$(1 \times 3, \; 12 \times 1) = (3,12) = (1,4).$$

CHAPTER EIGHT

Introducing the Rationals

THERE are many other numbers besides the *natural numbers* (0,1, 2, 3, . . .) and the *directed numbers*, or integers, (which can have negative values). The missing numbers lie in the gaps left between the natural numbers (or integers). They are called the *rationals*, because they are defined as ratios (one number divided by another number).

The missing numbers can easily be seen by plotting sets of numbers along the number line. The method also involves *mapping* one set of numbers on to the set of integers on the number line.

Suppose the upper set represents a distance in feet and the lower set a distance in yards. There are three 'foot' markings to every 'yard' marking. So two out of three foot markings do not correspond to any of the numbers on the yard line. It is obvious that they correspond to a third of a yard. But $\frac{1}{3}$ is neither a natural number nor an integer. What kind of number is it? It is often known as a *fraction* and, if 1 is divided by 3, by the decimal number $0 \cdot \dot{3}$ (nought-point-three-recurring). Yet another way of writing the number is as an *ordered pair* of numbers (1,3). These are all ways of writing rational numbers.

The *ordered pair* notation is perhaps the most useful and versatile. Fractions need *two* numbers (the numerator and denominator of the fraction) to define them. In the usual fractional form, the numbers are set one over the other. In the ordered pair notation, they are set one after the other.

Sets of Ordered Pairs

The set of rational numbers

$$\tfrac{1}{3}, \tfrac{2}{3}, \tfrac{3}{3}, \tfrac{4}{3}, \ldots$$

have one thing in common. They are all numbers of *thirds*. 3 is the denominator of each of the fractions. In other words, they all belong to the *set of thirds*.

A small part of the number line is examined on a larger scale. The 1 foot and 2 feet markings on one number line have no corresponding markings on the other number line.

Now the lower number line is marked in *rational* numbers or *ordered pairs* of numbers. 1 foot corresponds to $\tfrac{1}{3}$ yard. $\tfrac{1}{3}$ is written down as the ordered pair (1,3). The rationals fill in some of the space between the whole number markings.

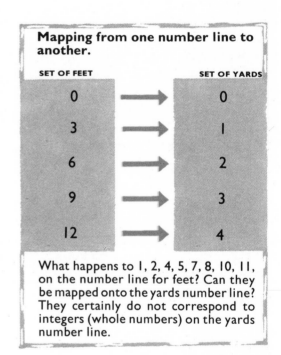

Mapping from one number line to another.

What happens to 1, 2, 4, 5, 7, 8, 10, 11, on the number line for feet? Can they be mapped onto the yards number line? They certainly do not correspond to integers (whole numbers) on the yards number line.

The number line for feet.

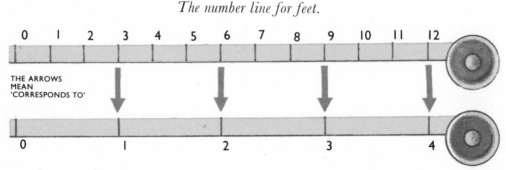

THE ARROWS MEAN 'CORRESPONDS TO'

The number line for yards. A number of feet correspond to a number of yards. Three feet correspond to one yard, and so on.

Ordered pairs form a useful set when the second number of the pair is the same for each ordered pair. In particular, this simplifies the rules for adding and subtracting the pairs.

In the *ordered pairs* notation, the same set is written as

$$(1,3), (2,3), (3,3), (4,3), \ldots$$

Three Ways of Looking at Rationals

As Fractions

$$\tfrac{1}{3}, \tfrac{2}{3}, \tfrac{3}{3}, \tfrac{4}{3}, \ldots$$

The number on top is the *numerator* and the number underneath, the *denominator*.

As Decimals

$$0 \cdot \dot{3}, 0 \cdot \dot{6}, 1 \cdot 0, 1 \cdot \dot{3}\dot{3} \ldots$$

These are the fractions based on tenths, hundredths, thousandths, and so on.

As Ordered Pairs

$$(1, 3), (2, 3), (3, 3), (4, 3), \ldots$$

The first number of the pair corresponds to the numerator of the fraction and the second number, the denominator. It also denotes the set of ordered pairs to which the pair belongs. If the denominator is 3, then the pair belongs to the set of thirds.

CHAPTER NINE

The Irrationals

IF A rational number is defined as a ratio in the form $\frac{m}{n}$, where m and n are integers, then a number which cannot be expressed as such a ratio is called an IRRATIONAL number. They appear only as mathematical expressions with an infinitely large number of digits. There are special ways of representing these numbers, sometimes by introducing them with special symbols and at other times by letters which have become synonymous with their meaning in mathematics.

Thus the *square root of 2 is written $\sqrt{2}$ and is a number which does not evaluate to a rational. The sign $\sqrt{}$ is the symbolic method of indicating the root extraction. A small figure placed

* See Chapter 16.

over the symbol $\sqrt[3]{}$ indicates the extent of the extraction required and in this case the cube root is required.

Rational numbers could be found by comparing markings on number lines – for example a number line marked in feet with a number line marked in yards to obtain the set of *thirds*,

$$(1, 3), (2, 3), (3, 3), (4, 3) \ldots$$

This method does not work for irrationals, because the position of any irrational on a number line can never be pin-pointed accurately. All that can be said of an irrational number is that it is bigger than a rational number to its left on the number line, and smaller than a rational number to its right.

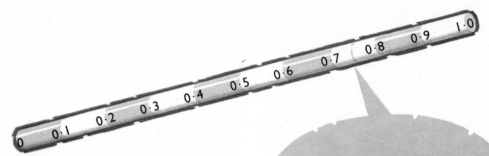

Rational Numbers

Some of the rational numbers between 0 and 1 are mapped on to the number line above. Rational numbers can be written either as fractions, decimals or ordered pairs.

This definite marking corresponds to the rational number

0.75 or $\frac{75}{100}$ or $\frac{3}{4}$

Irrational Numbers

π

π is an irrational number. It cannot be written as a ratio of two whole numbers.

Filling in the spaces on the number line

Each rational number can correspond to a mark on the number line. If all the rationals between 0 and 1 were marked by a line, the number line would be completely covered in marks, because the number of rationals possible is infinitely large.

But the number line appears covered only because of our clumsiness in drawing the marks – theoretically they should have no width at all. Empty spaces remain between the rationals, no matter how many of them are drawn in. The spaces are filled in by irrational numbers. They are in theory essential if the complete line is to be used for measuring lengths, in terms of any of the common units – the yard, foot, metre, or centimetre.

The number π

One very important irrational number is obtained when the circumference of a circle is divided by its diameter. This, though a ratio, does not come out to any well-defined value

30

and cannot be contained within any limits. The only conclusive result obtained from the ratio of the circumference of any circle to the diameter of the same circle is that the value is a constant quantity for any circle. This constant has been given the name pi and written π with a rough approximation of its value as $\frac{22}{7}$. A closer approximation is $\frac{355}{113}$. The investigations by mathematicians to try to find the exact value of π have been varied, painstaking, laborious, ingenious but unsuccessful. A mathematician who spent a large part of his life trying to fix a value for π had its value to 35 decimal places engraved on his tombstone in recognition of the work he did on it. Another geometer calculated its value to 15 decimal places by calculating the perimeter of a polygon of 2^{30} sides inscribed in a circle. The algebraists used infinite series of the form

$$\pi = 4(1 - \tfrac{1}{3} + \tfrac{1}{5} - \tfrac{1}{7} + \tfrac{1}{9} - \tfrac{1}{11} + \ldots)$$

to find its value. But in more recent times electronic brain machines have obtained the value of π to 10,000 places of decimals eclipsing the 707 decimal places obtained manually. Another interesting feature about the digits obtained in the value of π is that none of them is particularly favoured though all ten appear in the result.

Rationalisation

If $\sqrt{2}$ is multiplied by itself we have $\sqrt{2} \times \sqrt{2} = \sqrt{4} = 2$. Thus irrational quantities of this type can be made into other rational quantities in this way. This suggests an easy method of evaluating fractions with irrational denominators. This process is known as RATIONALISATION.

SOME USES OF IRRATIONAL NUMBERS

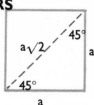

The diagonal of a square is always $\sqrt{2} \times$ side of the square

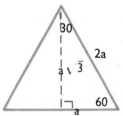

The diagonal of a cube is always $\sqrt{3} \times$ side of the cube

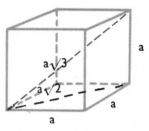

The height of an equilateral triangle is always $\sqrt{3} \times \frac{1}{2}$ the side of the triangle

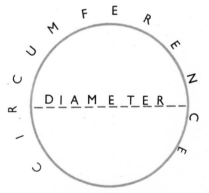

$$\pi = \frac{\text{CIRCUMFERENCE}}{\text{DIAMETER}}$$

$$\pi = \frac{\text{AREA}}{(\text{RADIUS})^2}$$

CHAPTER TEN

Mathematical Mapping

THE map of an area is a small-scale version of the area, as seen from the air. But it is not exactly the area in miniature. Only an aerial photograph gives this. In the map, a thick line corresponds to a road crossing the area. Black blocks correspond to houses and crosses to churches. Always, when making a map of something, the idea is to let small symbols on the map correspond to the real object.

In mathematics, mapping means a very similar thing. Mathematics can be used as a practical subject, to solve practical problems. Sorting out a problem about a number of pencils, or books, using the books themselves as the counters may be more instructive than solving the problem on pen and paper. But it can be slower and more cumbersome. It is sometimes better to *map* the problem into mathematical symbols and language. It is easier to juggle with numbers and symbols, because they are known to obey certain rules. Whenever we solve a problem about books, pencils or bricks by mathematics, we are *mapping the problem*.

The map of an area of countryside does not show all that can be seen from the air. Some features are mapped, and others are disregarded because they are unimportant. Mapping in mathematics is also *selective*. The main thing to learn is what to map in any given problem, and what irrelevant details to leave out.

The real objects are called the *original set* and their mapping is called

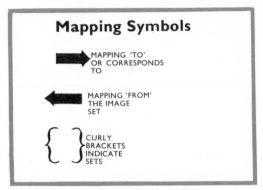

Mapping Symbols

MAPPING 'TO' OR CORRESPONDS TO

MAPPING 'FROM' THE IMAGE SET

{ } CURLY BRACKETS INDICATE SETS

The aerial view (above) is turned into the map (below). Objects of the original set are mapped to symbols of the image set. The mapping shows relative positions, relative distances, and so on. Some objects are not mapped.

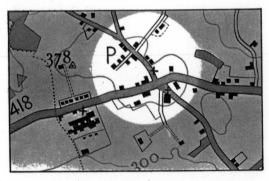

the *image set*. (A set is a collection of objects or numbers with something in common.) So, in mathematical language, a problem starts off in the original set, is mapped to the image set for solution, and then is mapped *from* the image set back to the original set.

Arranging the Map

The symbols on a map have to be arranged to correspond with the original. In mathematical mappings it is sometimes best to arrange the number of the image set in columns or tables. A shopping list is a simple example. Yet another kind of mapping is used by architects and civil engineers. For example, a draughtsman's drawing of a section of a bridge is a mapping of the bridge itself. The mapping can go a stage further by mapping the forces acting on each part of the section, to find the stresses and strains which the bridge must be able to withstand.

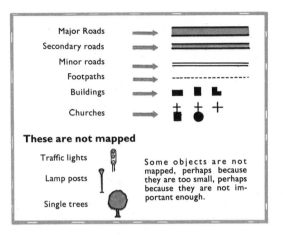

Major Roads	
Secondary roads	
Minor roads	
Footpaths	
Buildings	
Churches	

These are not mapped

Traffic lights

Lamp posts

Single trees

Some objects are not mapped, perhaps because they are too small, perhaps because they are not important enough.

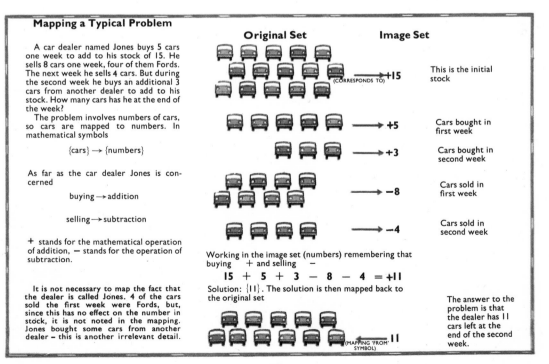

Mapping a Typical Problem

A car dealer named Jones buys 5 cars one week to add to his stock of 15. He sells 8 cars one week, four of them Fords. The next week he sells 4 cars. But during the second week he buys an additional 3 cars from another dealer to add to his stock. How many cars has he at the end of the week?

The problem involves numbers of cars, so cars are mapped to numbers. In mathematical symbols

$$\{cars\} \rightarrow \{numbers\}$$

As far as the car dealer Jones is concerned

$$buying \rightarrow addition$$

$$selling \rightarrow subtraction$$

+ stands for the mathematical operation of addition, − stands for the operation of subtraction.

It is not necessary to map the fact that the dealer is called Jones. 4 of the cars sold the first week were Fords, but, since this has no effect on the number in stock, it is not noted in the mapping. Jones bought some cars from another dealer – this is another irrelevant detail.

Original Set   **Image Set**

(CORRESPONDS TO) +15   This is the initial stock

+5   Cars bought in first week

+3   Cars bought in second week

−8   Cars sold in first week

−4   Cars sold in second week

Working in the image set (numbers) remembering that buying + and selling −

$$15 + 5 + 3 - 8 - 4 = +11$$

Solution: {11}. The solution is then mapped back to the original set

(MAPPING 'FROM' SYMBOL) 11

The answer to the problem is that the dealer has 11 cars left at the end of the second week.

CHAPTER ELEVEN

Sets and Venn Diagrams

SETS are groups of objects or numbers with properties in common. A simple example of a set is *pencil, crayon, ball-point pen, fountain pen*. They are all instruments used for writing. This is their property in common. An example of a mathematical set is the set of *natural* numbers.

1, 2, 3, 4 . . .

The *even natural* numbers

2, 4, 6, 8 . . .

also form a mathematical set. The property all the numbers of the set have in common is that they are all multiples of two.

The way of symbolizing a set of numbers or objects is:

{even natural numbers}

{natural numbers}

{writing instruments}

The curly brackets are to be read as 'the set of'.

If an object or number belongs to a set, then the mathematical way of writing down this fact is

pencil ∈ {writing instruments}

But it must be read as 'the pencil is an element that belongs to the set of writing instruments'. Another example is

2 ∈ {even natural numbers}

(2 is an element that belongs to the set of even natural numbers). The members of a set are called its *elements*.

Mapping from one Set to Another

When a geographical region is mapped, the set of real objects in the region is mapped to a set of symbols. The operation of mapping to a new set is symbolized by an arrow.

{Buildings, roads etc.} → {map symbols} A building in the region corresponds to a black block on the map, so the arrow also means 'corresponds to'.

Mathematics is often used to find solutions to real problems. The real problem comes from an original or *object set*. It is mapped to an *image set* of numbers for solution. A problem involving a number of books would be mapped as

{books} → {numbers}

It is possible to carry out calculations in {numbers} because if mathematical operations like addition and multiplication are carried out between elements of {numbers} the result always

Symbols

∈ means 'is an element of' e.g. ✏ ∈ {writing instruments}

∉ means 'is not an element of' e.g. 📖 ∉ {writing instruments}

∅ is the null set e.g. ∅ = {ten-footed people}

A∩B is the intersection of A and B, i.e. the elements which belong to both A and B.

A∪B is the union of A and B, i.e. the elements which belong to either A or B or both.

U is the universal set, to which all the elements under discussion belong.

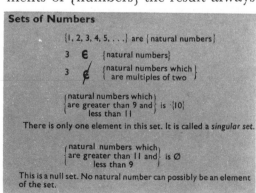

Sets of Numbers

{1, 2, 3, 4, 5, . . .} are {natural numbers}

3 ∈ {natural numbers}

3 ∉ {natural numbers which are multiples of two}

{natural numbers which are greater than 9 and less than 11} is {10}

There is only one element in this set. It is called a *singular set*.

{natural numbers which are greater than 11 and less than 9} is ∅

This is a null set. No natural number can possibly be an element of the set.

Venn Diagrams

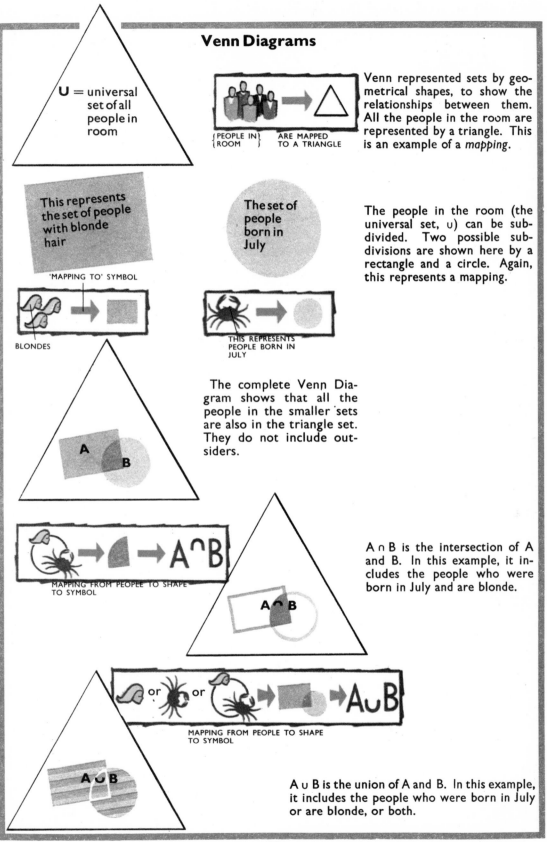

U = universal set of all people in room

PEOPLE IN ROOM — ARE MAPPED TO A TRIANGLE

Venn represented sets by geometrical shapes, to show the relationships between them. All the people in the room are represented by a triangle. This is an example of a *mapping*.

This represents the set of people with blonde hair

The set of people born in July

The people in the room (the universal set, u) can be subdivided. Two possible subdivisions are shown here by a rectangle and a circle. Again, this represents a mapping.

'MAPPING TO' SYMBOL

BLONDES

THIS REPRESENTS PEOPLE BORN IN JULY

The complete Venn Diagram shows that all the people in the smaller sets are also in the triangle set. They do not include outsiders.

A

B

MAPPING FROM PEOPLE TO SHAPE TO SYMBOL

→ A∩B

A ∩ B is the intersection of A and B. In this example, it includes the people who were born in July and are blonde.

A∩B

or ... or ... → A∪B

MAPPING FROM PEOPLE TO SHAPE TO SYMBOL

A∪B

A ∪ B is the union of A and B. In this example, it includes the people who were born in July or are blonde, or both.

Problems Mapped to Venn Diagrams

25

A

This is the set studying French.

17

B

This is the set studying German.

All the class of 30 English students are learning at least one foreign language. 17 are studying German, 25 are studying French. How many are studying both?

U

= universal set of 30 students

A ∪ B

30

All the class are studying either French or German, or both. The *union* of A and B (A ∪ B) is the set of either As or Bs or both As and Bs. So the union of A and B is {30}.

? **A ∩ B**

The problem is to find the intersection of A and B, the number studying both foreign languages. It is not difficult to see that this is the total of A and B, minus the *union* of A and B. This leaves the shaded area shown on the Venn Diagram.

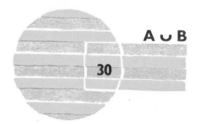

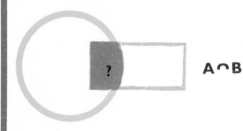

A   **+**   B   **−**   A ∪ B   **=**   A ∩ B

=   {12}

A ∩ B   **=**   {12}

The answer to the problem is that 12 pupils are studying both languages

belongs to the same set. The elements of the system of natural numbers have five basic properties in common. These cover the five possible ways of adding, subtracting, multiplying, dividing and collecting together the natural numbers. Providing no other operation is carried out, the result is always an element of the same set. The elements of {directed numbers} have similar properties.

When the result is found in the image set, it is mapped back to the object set. This is symbolized by an arrow in the opposite direction.

Venn Diagrams

John Venn was an English mathematician who died in 1924, and who made a particular study of sets. Venn represented sets by geometrical figures – circles, triangles and parallelograms. A triangle might represent the set of people in a room.

Sets like groups of people could often be subdivided into smaller sets, according to the colour of their hair, or their age group or the month in which they were born or by any other characteristic.

A circle might represent the set of people with birthdays in July, and a rectangle, people with blonde hair (see p. 35).

A Venn diagram is a way of arranging the geometrical shapes, the rectangle, triangle and circle, to show the relationships between the different sets. All the people with blonde hair and birthdays in July in the room belong to three sets – the rectangle, the triangle and the circle. All members of the rectangle set and circle set are also members of the triangle set. On the Venn diagram of this situation, both the rectangle and the circle fit inside the triangle.

CHAPTER TWELVE

Finite Series

AN arrangement of numbers whereby any number in it can be deduced according to a mathematical law is called a series. Two such different but typical series are:

(a) 1, 3, 5, 7, 9, 11
(b) 1, 2, 4, 8, 16, 32

The first is called an Arithmetic and the second a Geometric series. The Arithmetic series can be developed as shown below.

The number 2 is part of each term and the *difference* between successive pairs of terms is this number 2, and since it is common to all successive pairs of terms it is known as the

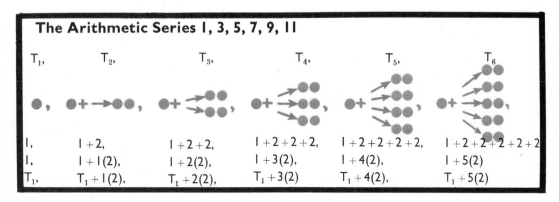

The Arithmetic Series 1, 3, 5, 7, 9, 11

T_1,	T_2,	T_3,	T_4,	T_5,	T_6
1,	1+2,	1+2+2,	1+2+2+2,	1+2+2+2+2,	1+2+2+2+2+2
1,	1+1(2),	1+2(2),	1+3(2),	1+4(2),	1+5(2)
T_1,	$T_1+1(2)$,	$T_1+2(2)$,	$T_1+3(2)$	$T_1+4(2)$,	$T_1+5(2)$

common difference of the series (d), each term containing one *additional* 2 than the term immediately preceding it. The number of 2's in each term is obtained by multiplying 2 by a number less by one than the number of the term. Thus:

term two, T_2, contains $1(2)$, one 2
term three, T_3, contains $2(2)$, two 2's
term four, T_4, contains $3(2)$, three 2's
and so on. Each term is made up of the first term plus the corresponding number of 2's. In general the series becomes

$$T_1 + 0(2),\ T_1 + 1(2),\ T_1 + 2(2),$$
$$T_1 + 3(2),\ T_1 + 4(2),\ T_1 + 5(2)$$

and the general term

$$T_n = T_1 + (n-1)d$$

where *n* has the values 1, 2, 3, 4, etc. and *d* has the constant value 2. Hence starting with any number and replacing the common difference number 2 by any other number, series of this type can be formed.

In the second or Geometric series each successive term is double the immediately preceding term.

The number 2 is present in each term and the *ratio* between successive pairs of terms is this number 2, and since it is common to all successive pairs of terms it is known as the common ratio (r), each term containing a power of 2 one higher than the term immediately preceding it. The *power* of 2 in each term is less by one than the number of the term.

Thus term two, T_2, contains $(2)^1$, first power of 2.
term three, T_3, contains $(2)^2$, second power of 2
term four, T_4, contains $(2)^3$, third power of 2

and so on. Each term is made up of the first term *multiplied* by the corresponding power of 2. In general the series becomes

$$T_1(2)^0,\ T_1(2)^1,\ T_1(2)^2,\ T_1(2)^3,$$
$$T_1(2)^4,\ T_1(2)^5$$

and the general term

$$T_n = T_1(r)^{n-1}$$

where n has the values 1, 2, 3, 4, etc.

Examples of Arithmetic Series

$T_1 = 5;\ d = -2$ giving the series

$$5,\quad 5 + 1(-2),\quad 5 + 2(-2),\quad 5 + 3(-2),\quad 5 + 4(-2),\quad 5 + 5(-2)$$

or $\quad 5,\qquad\quad 3,\qquad\qquad 1,\qquad\qquad -1,\qquad\qquad -3,\qquad\qquad -5$

$T_1 = -\frac{1}{2};\ d = \frac{1}{3}$ again giving the series

$$-\tfrac{1}{2},\quad -\tfrac{1}{2} + 1(\tfrac{1}{3}),\quad -\tfrac{1}{2} + 2(\tfrac{1}{3}),\quad -\tfrac{1}{2} + 3(\tfrac{1}{3}),\quad -\tfrac{1}{2} + 4(\tfrac{1}{3}),\quad -\tfrac{1}{2} + 5(\tfrac{1}{3})$$

or $\quad -\tfrac{1}{2},\qquad -\tfrac{1}{6},\qquad\quad \tfrac{1}{6},\qquad\qquad \tfrac{3}{6},\qquad\qquad \tfrac{5}{6},\qquad\qquad \tfrac{7}{6}$

or $\quad -\tfrac{1}{2},\qquad -\tfrac{1}{6},\qquad\quad \tfrac{1}{6},\qquad\qquad \tfrac{1}{2},\qquad\qquad \tfrac{5}{6},\qquad\qquad 1\tfrac{1}{6}$

Examples of Geometric Series

$T_1 = 5;\ r = -2$ giving the series

$$5,\quad 5(-2),\quad 5(-2)^2,\quad 5(-2)^3,\quad 5(-2)^4,\quad 5(-2)^5$$

or $\quad 5,\qquad -10,\qquad 20\qquad\quad -40,\qquad 80\qquad\quad -160$

$T_1 = -\frac{1}{2};\ r = \frac{1}{3}$ again giving the series

$$-\tfrac{1}{2},\quad -\tfrac{1}{2}(\tfrac{1}{3}),\quad -\tfrac{1}{2}(\tfrac{1}{3})^2,\quad -\tfrac{1}{2}(\tfrac{1}{3})^3,\quad -\tfrac{1}{2}(\tfrac{1}{3})^4,\quad -\tfrac{1}{2}(\tfrac{1}{3})^5,$$

or $\quad -\tfrac{1}{2},\qquad -\tfrac{1}{6},\qquad\quad -\tfrac{1}{18},\qquad -\tfrac{1}{54},\qquad -\tfrac{1}{162},\qquad -\tfrac{1}{486}$

Hence starting with any number and replacing the common ratio 2 by any other number, series of this type can be formed.

The Geometric Series 1, 2, 4, 8, 16, 32

T_1,	T_2,	T_3,	T_4,	T_5,	T_6
1,	1×2,	$1 \times 2 \times 2$,	$1 \times 2 \times 2 \times 2$,	$1 \times 2 \times 2 \times 2 \times 2$,	$1 \times 2 \times 2 \times 2 \times 2 \times 2$
1,	$1 \times (2)^1$,	$1 \times (2)^2$,	$1 \times (2)^3$,	$1 \times (2)^4$,	$1 \times (2)^5$
T_1,	$T_1 \times (2)^1$,	$T_1 \times (2)^2$,	$T_1 \times (2)^3$,	$T_1 \times (2)^4$,	$T_1 \times (2)^5$

Some Common Series Investigated

SERIES	T_6	T_n (general term)	T_{50}
1, 3, 5, 7, 9,	11	$T_1 + (n - 1)\,d$	$1 + (49 \times 2) = 99$
1, 2, 4, 8, 16 $2^0, 2^1, 2^2, 2^3, 2^4$	32 2^5	$T_1 (r)^{n-1}$	$1.(2)^{49}$
$\dfrac{1}{2}, \dfrac{2}{3}, \dfrac{3}{4}, \dfrac{4}{5}, \dfrac{5}{6}$	$\dfrac{6}{7}$	$\dfrac{n}{n+1}$	$\dfrac{50}{51}$
$\dfrac{2}{3}, \dfrac{4}{9}, \dfrac{6}{27}, \dfrac{8}{81}, \dfrac{10}{243}$	$\dfrac{12}{729}$	$\dfrac{2n}{3^n}$	$\dfrac{100}{3^{50}}$
$\dfrac{2}{3}, \dfrac{4}{3^2}, \dfrac{6}{3^3}, \dfrac{8}{3^4}, \dfrac{10}{3^5}$	$\dfrac{12}{3^6}$		
1, 4, 9, 16, 25	36	n^2	50^2
$1^2, 2^2, 3^2, 4^2, 5^2$	6^2		
25, 36, 49, 64, 81	100	$(n + 4)^2$	54^2
$5^2, 6^2, 7^2, 8^2, 9^2$	10^2		
1, 8, 27, 64, 125	216	n^3	50^3
$1^3, 2^3, 3^3, 4^3, 5^3$	6^3		
3, 15, 35, 63, 99	143	$(2n - 1)(2n + 1)$	99×101
$1 \times 3, 3 \times 5, 5 \times 7, 7 \times 9, 9 \times 11$	11×13		
28, 80, 162, 280, 440	648	$n(n + 3)(n + 6)$	$50 \times 53 \times 56$
1.4.7, 2.5.8, 3.6.9, 4.7.10, 5.8.11	6.9.12		

Summation of Series

No series is of very much value unless its sum can be evaluated. Two stories here will not be out of place to make this clear.

It used to be quite standard practice for senior members, monitors and prefects of a school to give very junior members, who had fallen foul of the laws governing good discipline in a school, the task of adding up all the numbers from 1 to 100 or even 1 to 1,000, depending on the severity of the young rascals' crimes. After laborious additions, wrong answers and wasted hours by these young innocents, the result was obtained by the knowledgeable big boys in a matter of seconds.

$$S_{100} = \frac{100}{2}(1 + 100)$$
$$= 50 \times 101 = 5050$$

The second story relates to the geometric series and tells of a rich Eastern potentate who was being taught how to play the game of chess by its inventor. He was so fascinated by the game that he asked his mentor to name any reward of his choosing and he would supply it. The inventor placed a grain of rice on the first square, two on the second, four on the third and said that all he wanted was that the number of grains of rice be doubled on each square and so on throughout the board. The rich man was nonplussed that he should ask for so little reward for such a marvellous invention. However, as it was his wish the potentate ordered that the inventor's wish should be immediately complied with. But it came as a great shock to him when he was informed that there was not sufficient rice in all his granaries to pay the reward, and the quantity required would cover the entire surface of the earth with enough left over to feed the starving

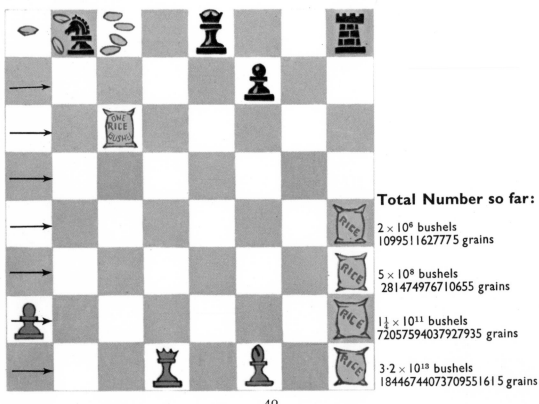

Total Number so far:

2×10^6 bushels
10995116277 75 grains

5×10^8 bushels
281474976710655 grains

$1\frac{1}{4} \times 10^{11}$ bushels
72057594037927935 grains

$3 \cdot 2 \times 10^{13}$ bushels
18446744073709551615 grains

population of the world.

$$S_{64} = (2^{64} - 1)$$
$$= 18,446,744,073,709,551,615$$

grains.

Development of the Series for Addition

The Arithmetic series

$$S_6 = 1 + 3 + 5 + 7 + 9 + 11$$
$$S_6 = 11 + 9 + 7 + 5 + 3 + 1$$

$$\text{Adding } 2S_6 = 12 + 12 + 12 + 12 + 12 + 12$$
$$= 6 \times 12$$
$$= 6 \times (1 + 11)$$
$$S_6 = \frac{6}{2} \times (1 + 11)$$

Analysing this result we find that 6 is the number of terms added, 1 is the first term and 11 the last term. Extending this to any number of terms we have

$$S_n = \frac{\text{number of terms}}{2} \text{ (first term + last term)}$$

$$S_n = \frac{n}{2}(T_1 + T_L)$$

but $T_L = T_1 + (n-1)d$

$$\therefore \quad S_n = \frac{n}{2}\left\{T_1 + T_1 + (n-1)d\right\}$$

$$S_n = \frac{n}{2}\left\{2T_1 + (n-1)d\right\}$$

The Geometric series

$$S_6 = T_1 + 2T_1 + 2^2T_1 + 2^3T_1 + 2^4T_1 + 2^5T_1 \ldots (i)$$

Equation (i) × 2 gives:

$$2S_6 = 2T_1 + 2^2T_1 + 2^3T_1 + 2^4T_1 + 2^5T_1 + 2^6T_1 \text{ (ii)}$$

Subtracting (i) from (ii) gives:

$$S_6(2-1) = 2^6T_1 - T_1 = T_1(2^6 - 1)$$

$$S_6 = \frac{T_1(2^6 - 1)}{(2-1)}$$

Analysing this result we find that 6 is the number of terms added and 2 the common ratio. Extending this to any number of terms we have

$$S_n = \frac{\text{first term (ratio}^{\text{number of terms}} - 1)}{(\text{ratio} - 1)}$$

$$S_n = \frac{T_1(r^n - 1)}{(r - 1)}$$

Some other series summed

$$S_6 = 1.2 + 2.3 + 3.4 + 4.5 + 5.6 + 6.7$$

$$1.2.3 - 0.1.2 = (1.2).3$$
$$2.3.4 - 1.2.3 = (2.3).3$$
$$3.4.5 - 2.3.4 = (3.4).3$$
$$4.5.6 - 3.4.5 = (4.5).3$$
$$5.6.7 - 4.5.6 = (5.6).3$$
$$6.7.8 - 5.6.7 = (6.7).3$$

$$\text{Adding } 6.7.8 \qquad = 3.S_6$$

$$\therefore \quad S_6 = \frac{1}{3}(6.7.8)$$

The number 6 is the number of the terms added in the series. Extending this to any number of terms we have

$$S_n = \frac{1}{3}n(n+1)(n+2)$$

$$S_6 = 1.2.3 + 2.3.4 + 3.4.5 + 4.5.6 + 5.6.7 + 6.7.8$$

$$1.2.3.4 - 0.1.2.3 = (1.2.3).4$$
$$2.3.4.5 - 1.2.3.4 = (2.3.4).4$$
$$3.4.5.6 - 2.3.4.5 = (3.4.5).4$$
$$4.5.6.7 - 3.4.5.6 = (4.5.6).4$$
$$5.6.7.8 - 4.5.6.7 = (5.6.7).4$$
$$6.7.8.9 - 5.6.7.8 = (6.7.8).4$$

$$\text{Adding } 6.7.8.9 \qquad = 4S_6$$

$$\therefore \quad S_6 = \frac{1}{4}(6.7.8.9)$$

Again the number 6 is the number of the terms added in the series. Extending this to any number of terms we have

$$S_n = \frac{1}{4}n(n+1)(n+2)(n+3)$$

Sum of the squares of the natural numbers

$$S_6 = 1^2 + 2^2 + 3^2 + 4^2 + 5^2 + 6^2$$

$$1.2 - 1 = 1^2$$
$$2.3 - 2 = 2^2$$
$$3.4 - 3 = 3^2$$
$$4.5 - 4 = 4^2$$
$$5.6 - 5 = 5^2$$
$$6.7 - 6 = 6^2$$

$$\text{Adding } \quad \frac{1}{3}(6.7.8) - \frac{6}{2}(1+6) = S_6$$

$$\text{Generally } \frac{1}{3}n(n+1)(n+2) - \frac{n}{2}(1+n) = S_n$$

$$\frac{n}{6}(n+1)[2(n+2) - 3] = S_n$$

$$\frac{n}{6}(n+1)(2n+1) = S_n$$

Sum of the cubes of the natural numbers

$$S_6 = 1^3 + 2^3 + 3^3 + 4^3 + 5^3 + 6^3$$

$$1.2.3 - 3.1^2 - 2.1 = 1^3$$
$$2.3.4 - 3.2^2 - 2.2 = 2^3$$
$$3.4.5 - 3.3^2 - 2.3 = 3^3$$
$$4.5.6 - 3.4^2 - 2.4 = 4^3$$
$$5.6.7 - 3.5^2 - 2.5 = 5^3$$
$$6.7.8 - 3.6^2 - 2.6 = 6^3$$

Sums of all these series have already been found.

Adding

$$\frac{1}{4}(6.7.8.9) - 3\left[\frac{1}{3}(6.7.8) - \frac{6}{2}(1+6)\right] - 2\left[\frac{6}{2}(1+6)\right] = S_6$$

$$\frac{1}{4}(6.7.8.9) - (6.7.8) + \frac{6}{2}(6+1) = S_6$$

Generally

$$\frac{1}{4}(n)(n+1)(n+2)(n+3) - n(n+1)(n+2) + \left(\frac{n}{2}\right)(n+1) = S_n$$

$$\frac{1}{4}n(n+1)[(n+2)(n+3) - 4(n+2) + 2] = S_n$$

$$\frac{1}{4}n(n+1)[(n^2 + 5n + 6 - 4n - 8 + 2] = S_n$$

$$S_n = \frac{1}{4}n(n+1)(n^2 + n)$$

$$= \frac{1}{4}n(n+1) \times n(n+1)$$

$$= \frac{1}{2}n(n+1) \times \frac{1}{2}n(n+1)$$

$$S_n = \left[\frac{n(n+1)}{2}\right]^2$$

CHAPTER THIRTEEN

Converging and Diverging Series

THE series of numbers $1 + 2 + 3 + 4 + 5$ and so on is a *diverging* series. The numbers (or *terms*) in the series get bigger and bigger, and the sum of all the terms increases cause the sum of all the terms in the series converges to a definite limit.

For the series to be converging, the terms must naturally become smaller and smaller. But this alone is not

A converging Series

This is the series $\frac{1}{2} + \frac{1}{4} + \frac{1}{8} + \frac{1}{16} + \ldots$ Each of the measures contains half as much as the previous one. The gallon bucket will never overflow. As more and more measures are emptied into it, it becomes more and more nearly full. Since it never overfills, the series is convergent.

I gallon (empty)

½ gallon

¼ gallon

⅛ gallon

1/16

rapidly. The series of numbers

$$\frac{1}{1} + \frac{1}{2} + \frac{1}{3} + \frac{1}{4}$$

and so on is also a *diverging* series. Although the individual terms in the series become smaller and smaller, the sum of the series continues to grow. It grows more slowly than the first series, but it still grows. Series where the sum continues to grow more as more terms are added on are called *diverging* series.

However, the sum of another kind of series does not increase indefinitely, and approaches a definite limit, no matter how many more terms in the series are added on. These are called *converging series*, be-

I gallon bucket

(NEARLY FULL)

½ gallon

¼ gallon

⅛

1/16

enough to ensure that the series is converging. Additional tests for the series are necessary.

Not all the series go on and on until there is an infinite number of terms in them. Some series stop after a few terms. It is then possible to get a definite sum to the series. *Convergency* and *divergency* apply only to series which never stop, but go on collecting an infinite number of terms. In all series, when the first few terms are given, the pattern for all the following terms is set.

Why Sum Series?

Series are of more than just interest

of it has 25, arranged in a 5×5 square and so on. The number of layers gives the number of terms in the series, and the total number of cannon balls can be calculated quite easily.

Convergent series are useful because they are used to track down numbers which can never be written down accurately, no matter how many decimal places are used. The number $\frac{10}{3}$ is one example. If ten is divided by 3, the result is:—

$3 \cdot 33333333333333333333333333333 \cdots$
or $3 \cdot \dot{3}$ – three decimal three recurring. There is no end to the number, because '1' is always 'carried on' when

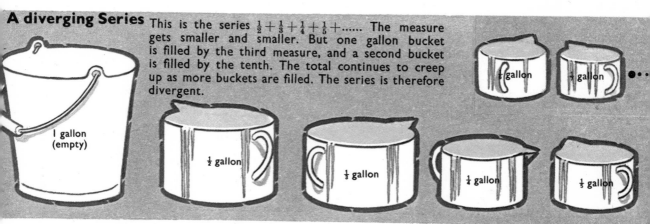

A diverging Series This is the series $\frac{1}{2} + \frac{1}{3} + \frac{1}{4} + \frac{1}{5} + \ldots$ The measure gets smaller and smaller. But one gallon bucket is filled by the third measure, and a second bucket is filled by the tenth. The total continues to creep up as more buckets are filled. The series is therefore divergent.

value. Once the pattern behind the series is known, it is possible to find the sum of any number of terms in it. The pattern of the series 1, 5, 14, 30, 55, 91, and so on is not obvious at first sight. In fact, the connection between these numbers is that they are basically a sequence of the *squares* of ordinary numbers (i.e. 1, 4, 9, 16, 25, 36 . . . and so on) with the sum of all its preceding terms added on. This kind of series was useful in working out the number of cannon balls which could be stacked in a square-based pyramid, of known height. If the bottom layer has 36 cannon balls arranged in a 6×6 square, the layer fitting on top

Converging series do not need to have an odd-looking number as their sum. It is possible to get a series containing an infinitely large number of terms, which gives, simply, I as its total.

This series is

$$\frac{1}{2}+\frac{1}{4}+\frac{1}{8}+\frac{1}{16}+\frac{1}{32}+\frac{1}{64}+\cdots$$

The sum of the series is I. A metre rule is one metre long. Half of the metre rule is equivalent to the first term. Add on half of the remaining part of the ruler (quarter of a metre) and the rule is threequarters of a metre long, an extra eighth and a sixteenth, and the rule becomes nearer and nearer the whole metre long.

10 is divided by 3.

Once a few decimal places are known, the number is accurate enough for most purposes. Although the number is difficult to write down accurately, it is nevertheless a definite number. It is easy to see that 3·3 recurring is just the series

$$3+\frac{3}{10}+\frac{3}{10^2}+\frac{3}{10^3}+\frac{3}{10^4}+\frac{3}{10^5}+\frac{3}{10^6}+\cdots$$

and so on. This is a converging series. Each term is ten times smaller than the previous one. All the tests for convergency prove that the sum of this series does approach a definite limit, the number being equal to 10 divided by 3.

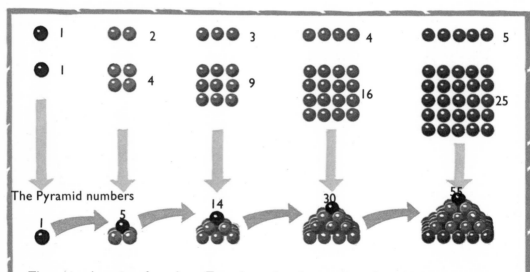

Three simple series of numbers. Top: the series of natural numbers. Middle: the squares of the natural numbers. Lower diagram: the pyramid numbers, formed from sums of squares. All the terms increase in size, so the series are all *divergent*.

CHAPTER FOURTEEN

Congruent and Similar Triangles

TRIANGLES that will fit snugly into the same mould must be identical in shape and size. Identical triangles are given the name *Congruent*. If the longest side of one of a pair of congruent triangles is a foot long, then the longest side of the other triangle must be exactly the same length. An angle of 30° in one triangle means an angle of 30° in the other. Any measurements will match up exactly if the triangles are congruent and there are *seven* common measurements, three sides, three angles and the area. Deciding by guesswork that two triangles look identical and working on from there is no good at all. Before any calculations can be made there must be real proof that they are identical. To prove congruency it is not necessary to make elaborate measurements and calculations of all seven dimensions; just three sets of corresponding measurements will suffice to prove triangles congruent and this is because three properties of any triangle will completely define it providing the three properties are one of the following sets:

(*a*) three sides (S.S.S.)

(*b*) two angles and one side (A.A.S.), and

(*c*) two sides and the angle made by these two sides, known as the *included angle*.

Right-angled Triangles

When drawing a right-angled triangle only *two* additional properties need be applied to the triangle to completely define it and they are the hypotenuse (the side opposite the right angle) and either of the remaining two sides.

The Ambiguous Case

If we try to draw a triangle given

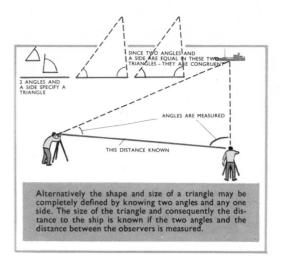

Alternatively the shape and size of a triangle may be completely defined by knowing two angles and any one side. The size of the triangle and consequently the distance to the ship is known if the two angles and the distance between the observers is measured.

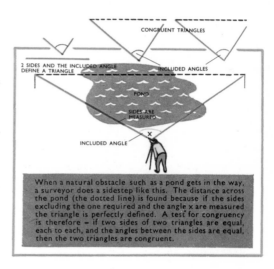

When a natural obstacle such as a pond gets in the way, a surveyor does a sidestep like this. The distance across the pond (the dotted line) is found because if the sides excluding the one required and the angle x are measured the triangle is perfectly defined. A test for congruency is therefore – if two sides of two triangles are equal, each to each, and the angles between the sides are equal, then the two triangles are congruent.

two sides and an angle which is *not* included by these two sides, we can draw *two* triangles satisfying these conditions and there is therefore some

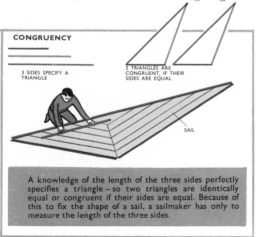

A knowledge of the length of the three sides perfectly specifies a triangle – so two triangles are identically equal or congruent if their sides are equal. Because of this to fix the shape of a sail, a sailmaker has only to measure the length of the three sides.

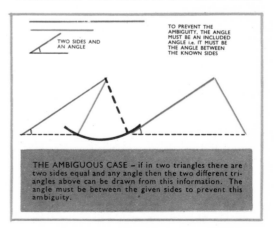

THE AMBIGUOUS CASE – if in two triangles there are two sides equal and any angle then the two different triangles above can be drawn from this information. The angle must be between the given sides to prevent this ambiguity.

ambiguity about which of the two triangles is being considered for comparison. The ambiguous case can be identified in the following manner. Three conditions must be satisfied, they are:

(1) two sides and an angle (not included) must be known,

(2) the known angle must be *acute*, and

(3) the known side opposite the known angle must be smaller than the other known side.

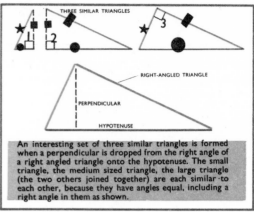

An interesting set of three similar triangles is formed when a perpendicular is dropped from the right angle of a right angled triangle onto the hypotenuse. The small triangle, the medium sized triangle, the large triangle (the two others joined together) are each similar to each other, because they have angles equal, including a right angle in them as shown.

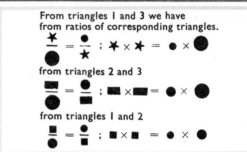

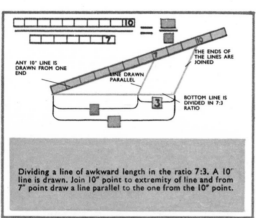

Dividing a line of awkward length in the ratio 7:3. A 10″ line is drawn. Join 10″ point to extremity of line and from 7″ point draw a line parallel to the one from the 10″ point.

Similar Triangles

Two triangles may seem to have the same shape but be different in size. They have the same shape because their corresponding angles are equal.

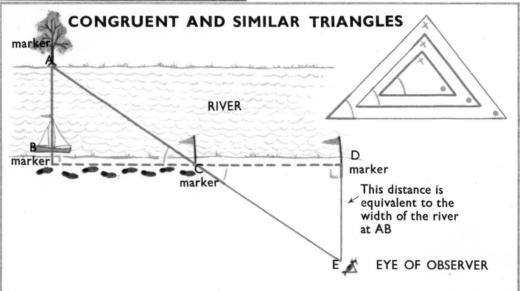

CONGRUENT AND SIMILAR TRIANGLES

A, B, C and D are suitably chosen markers. The triangles ABC and DCE are equiangular and hence similar. The ratios of corresponding sides are equal. The distances BC, CD are measured equal and therefore DE and AB are equal.

The triangles are thus miniatures or enlargements of one another. They are not identical and therefore cannot be congruent. The triangles are said to be *similar*. Surveyors use pairs of similar triangles in their calculations of distances, and astronomers use them to calculate the distance between stars and planets. Similar triangles are not only equiangular but have the ratios of their corresponding sides equal and it is this property which is so useful in making calculations.

CHAPTER FIFTEEN

The Parallelogram Family

The Birth Certificate

A birth certificate gives particulars of name, sex, date and place of birth of human beings. These particulars are attested and recorded for posterity. The facts are indisputable and form a basis for any future argument. Now if we had to give a parallelogram a birth certificate it would be described as the space enclosed by two pairs of parallel lines and would be accompanied by this photograph:

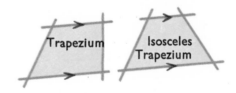

This forms the basis for any future argument. This is called the IN-TRINSIC property of the parallelogram. Now if we tried to enclose a space by four straight lines drawn at random observing the definition of a parallelogram, these are some of the shapes we could obtain:

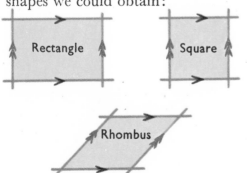

All these shapes have one thing in common, namely two pairs of parallel sides. They all differ in detail from the parallelogram and indeed from one another. Their names are the rectangle, the square, and the rhombus.

Now suppose we relax the discipline of having both pairs of lines parallel and restrict our drawings to having only one pair of sides parallel but still using four lines, then we would obtain two more figures thus:

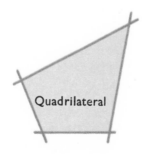

If we now give complete freedom to the drawing of the lines, then we arrive at the last of our four line shapes.

47

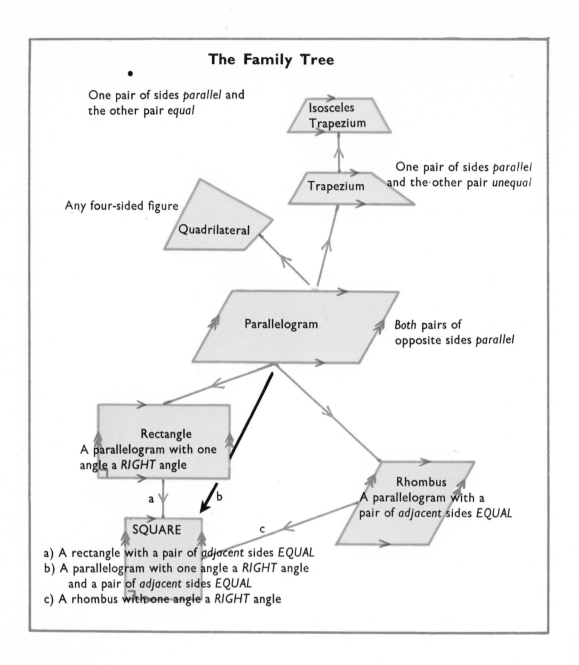

The Family Tree

All these figures belong to the family of four-sided figures with the parallelogram as the head of the family and the quadrilateral the ugly duckling. The additional markings on the figures help to indicate the contrasts and similarities between the figures.

These definitions are the basic requirements to identify the different figures, but as a result of these fundamental properties others can be proved for each figure distinguishing them one from the other in meticulous detail. A detailed study of the diagonals of these figures helps considerably to heighten these contrasts and similarities.

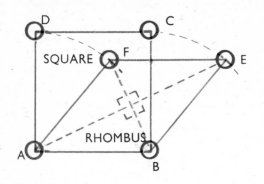

The Square-Rhombus Relationship

If the square were made out of joined rods, held firmly at the base corners and pressure applied at an opposite corner then the figure would distort to a rhombus.

Though the lengths of the diagonals change, one becoming bigger and the other smaller than that of the original square, they still continue to bisect each other at right angles.

Diagonal Relationships					
Figures / Diagonals	Parallelogram	Rectangle	Square	Rhombus	Isosceles Trapezium
(1) Length	unequal	equal	equal	unequal	equal
(2) Intersection	bisect each other at *any* angle	bisect each other at *any* angle	bisect each other at *right* angles	bisect each other at *right* angles	do *not* bisect each other
(3) Relation to base angle	does *not* bisect it	does *not* bisect it	does bisect it	does bisect it	does *not* bisect it

CHAPTER SIXTEEN

Square Roots

A LINE 3 units long is drawn horizontally. From one of the ends of this line another line 3 units long is drawn vertically. The two lines form two adjacent sides of a square and the area of the square is 9 square units. 9 is called the *square* of 3, for it is the number of square units in a square of side 3 units. The square of any number is the result of multiplying the number by itself. The square of 3 is $3 \times 3 = 9$; the square of 6 is $6 \times 6 = 36$ and so on. If we reverse the process then 6 is the *square root* of 36; 3 the *square root* of 9 and so on. The *square root* of any number can be imagined as the side

of a square of area containing that number of square units. Only a small proportion of numbers are 'perfect squares', that is numbers which have whole number square roots, and therefore finding the square root of any number is quite a special problem. The easiest way of finding the, perhaps approximate, square root of a number is to refer to square root tables.

How to Read the Tables

If the number is greater than one and contains an *odd* number of *digits* read the values for the *left* hand set of figures and for numbers containing an *even* number of *digits* read the values

SQUARE ROOTS

	0	1	2	3	4	5	6	7	8	9	1 2 3	4 5 6	7 8 9
75	2739	2740	2742	2744	2746	2748	2750	2751	2753	2755	0 0 1	1 1 1	1 1 2
76	2757	2759	2760	2762	2764	2766	2768	2769	2771	2773	0 0 1	1 1 1	1 1 2
77	2775	2777	2778	2780	2782	2784	2786	2787	2789	2791	0 0 1	1 1 1	1 1 2
78	2793	2795	2796	2798	2800	2802	2804	2805	2807	2809	0 0 1	1 1 1	1 1 2
79	2811	2812	2814	2816	2818	2820	2821	2823	2825	2827	0 0 1	1 1 1	1 1 2
80	2828	2830	2832	2834	2835	2837	2839	2841	2843	2844	0 0 1	1 1 1	1 1 2
81	2846	2848	2850	2851	2853	2855	2857	2858	2860	2862	0 0 1	1 1 1	1 1 2
82	2864	2865	2867	2869	2871	2872	2874	2876	2877	2879	0 0 1	1 1 1	1 1 2
83	2881	2883	2884	2886	2888	2890	2891	2893	2895	2897	0 0 1	1 1 1	1 1 2
84	2898	2900	2902	2903	2905	2907	2909	2910	2912	2914	0 0 1	1 1 1	1 1 2
85	2915	2917	2919	2921	2922	2924	2926	2927	2929	2931	0 0 1	1 1 1	1 1 2
86	2933	2934	2936	2938	2939	2941	2943	2944	2946	2948	0 0 1	1 1 1	1 1 2
87	2950	2951	2953	2955	2956	2958	2960	2961	2963	2965	0 0 1	1 1 1	1 1 2
88	2966	2968	2970	2972	2973	2975	2977	2978	2980	2982	0 0 1	1 1 1	1 1 2
89	2983	2985	2987	2988	2990	2992	2993	2995	2997	2998	0 0 1	1 1 1	1 1 2
90	3000	3002	3003	3005	3007	3008	3010	3012	3013	3015	0 0 0	1 1 1	1 1 1

SQUARE ROOTS

	0	1	2	3	4	5	6	7	8	9	1 2 3	4
75	8660	8666	8672	8678	8683	8689	8695	8701	8706	8712	1 1 2	2
76	8718	8724	8729	8735	8741	8746	8752	8758	8764	8769	1 1 2	2
77	8775	8781	8786	8792	8798	8803	8809	8815	8820	8826	1 1 2	2
78	8832	8837	8843	8849	8854	8860	8866	8871	8877	8883	1 1 2	2
79	8888	8894	8899	8905	8911	8916	8922	8927	8933	8939	1 1 2	2
80	8944	8950	8955	8961	8967	8972	8978	8983	8989	8994	1 1 2	2
81	9000	9006	9011	9017	9022	9028	9033	9039	9044	9050	1 1 2	2
82	9055	9061	9066	9072	9077	9083	9088	9094	9099	9105	1 1 2	2
83	9110	9116	9121	9127	9132	9138	9143	9149	9154	9160	1 1 2	2
84	9165	9171	9176	9182	9187	9192	9198	9203	9209	9214	1 1 2	2
85	9220	9225	9230	9236	9241	9247	9252	9257	9263	9268	1 1 2	2
86	9274	9279	9284	9290	9295	9301	9306	9311	9317	9322	1 1 2	2
87	9327	9333	9338	9343	9349	9354	9359	9365	9370	9375	1 1 2	2
88	9381	9386	9391	9397	9402	9407	9413	9418	9423	9429	1 1 2	2
89	9434	9439	9445	9450	9455	9460	9466	9471	9476	9482	1 1 2	2
90	9487	9492	9497	9503	9508	9513	9518	9524	9529	9534	1 1 2	2

NUMBER				Digits before decimal point in square root	Four significant figures			Table reading	Squar
77,847	7	78	47	3 digits	77	85	0	2789 + 1 = 2790	27
865,439	86	54	39	3 digits	86	54	00	9301 + 2 = 9303	93

The symbol for square roots is √
thus √77847 is 279.0
and √865439 is 930.2

ADD

	0	1	2	3	4	5	6	7	8	9	1 2 3	4 5 6	7 8 9
55	2345	2347	2349	2352	2354	2356	2358	2360	2362	2364	0 0 1	1 1 1	1 2 2
56	2366	2369	2371	2373	2375	2377	2379	2381	2383	2385	0 0 1	1 1 1	1 2 2
57	2387	2390	2392	2394	2396	2398	2400	2402	2404	2406	0 0 1	1 1 1	1 2 2
58	2408	2410	2412	2415	2417	2419	2421	2423	2425	2427	0 0 1	1 1 1	1 2 2
59	2429	2431	2433	2435	2437	2439	2441	2443	2445	2447	0 0 1	1 1 1	1 2 2
60	2449	2452	2454	2456	2458	2460	2462	2464	2466	2468	0 0 1	1 1 1	1 2 2
61	2470	2472	2474	2476	2478	2480	2482	2484	2486	2488	0 0 1	1 1 1	1 2 2
62	2490	2492	2494	2496	2498	2500	2502	2504	2506	2508	0 0 1	1 1 1	1 2 2
63	2510	2512	2514	2516	2518	2520	2522	2524	2526	2528	0 0 1	1 1 1	1 2 2
64	2530	2532	2534	2536	2538	2540	2542	2544	2546	2548	0 0 1	1 1 1	1 2 2
65	2550	2551	2553	2555	2557	2559	2561	2563	2565	2567	0 0 1	1 1 1	1 2 2
66	2569	2571	2573	2575	2577	2579	2581	2583	2585	2587	0 0 1	1 1 1	1 2 2
67	2588	2590	2592	2594	2596	2598	2600	2602	2604	2606	0 0 1	1 1 1	1 2 2
68	2608	2610	2612	2613	2615	2617	2619	2621	2623	2625	0 0 1	1 1 1	1 2 2
69	2627	2629	2631	2632	2634	2636	2638	2640	2642	2644	0 0 1	1 1 1	1 2 2
70	2646	2648	2650	2651	2653	2655	2657	2659	2661	2663	0 0 1	1 1 1	1 2 2
71	2665	2666	2668	2670	2672	2674	2676	2678	2680	2681	0 0 1	1 1 1	1 1 2
72	2683	2685	2687	2689	2691	2693	2696	2698	2700		0 0 1	1 1 1	1 1 2
73	2702	2704	2706	2707	2709	2711	2713	2715	2717	2718	0 0 1	1 1 1	1 1 2
74	2720	2722	2724	2726	2728	2729	2731	2733	2735	2737	0 0 1	1 1 1	1 1 2

	0	1	2	3	4	5	6	7	8	9	1 2 3	4 5
55	7416	7423	7430	7436	7443	7450	7457	7463	7470	7477	1 1 2	3 3
56	7483	7490	7497	7503	7510	7517	7523	7530	7537	7543	1 1 2	3 3
57	7550	7556	7563	7570	7576	7583	7589	7596	7603	7609	1 1 2	3 3
58	7616	7622	7629	7635	7642	7649	7655	7662	7668	7675	1 1 2	3 3
59	7681	7688	7694	7701	7707	7714	7720	7727	7733	7740	1 1 2	3 3
60	7746	7752	7759	7765	7772	7778	7785	7791	7797	7804	1 1 2	3 3
61	7810	7817	7823	7829	7836	7842	7849	7855	7861	7868	1 1 2	3 3
62	7874	7880	7887	7893	7899	7906	7912	7918	7925	7931	1 1 2	3 3
63	7937	7944	7950	7956	7962	7969	7975	7981	7987	7994	1 1 2	3 3
64	8000	8006	8012	8019	8025	8031	8037	8044	8050	8056	1 1 2	2 3
65	8062	8068	8075	8081	8087	8093	8099	8106	8112	8118	1 1 2	2 3
66	8124	8130	8136	8142	8149	8155	8161	8167	8173	8179	1 1 2	2 3
67	8185	8191	8198	8204	8210	8216	8222	8228	8234	8240	1 1 2	2 3
68	8246	8252	8258	8264	8270	8276	8283	8289	8295	8301	1 1 2	2 3
69	8307	8313	8319	8325	8331	8337	8343	8349	8355	8361	1 1 2	2 3
70	8367	8373	8379	8385	8390	8396	8402	8408	8414	8420	1 1 2	2 3
71	8426	8432	8438	8444	8450	8456	8462	8468	8473	8479	1 1 2	2 3
72	8485	8491	8497	8503	8509	8515	8521	8526	8532	8538	1 1 2	2 3
73	8544	8550	8556	8562	8567	8573	8579	8585	8591	8597	1 1 2	2 3
74	8602	8608	8614	8620	8626	8631	8637	8643	8649	8654	1 1 2	2 3

NUMBER	Square root first significant figure	Square root reading from tables
	By inspection	
7·	2·	2·646
'70·	8·	8·367
7'00·	2?·	26·46
70'00·	8?·	83·67
7'00'00·	2??·	264·6
70'00'00·	8??·	836·7
7'00'00'00·	2???·	2646·
70'00'00'00·	8???·	8367·

for the *right* hand set of figures. The table is in three parts; the first part records values for the first *two* digits, the second part for the *third* digit and the third part for the *fourth* digit of the number. As these are four figure tables any number of more than four digits must first be approximated to 4 significant figures. The number is now divided up from the right by grouping the digits in pairs, an odd number of digits will leave a single number in the last group reading from the right. Each group will give a single digit in the result for the square root.

TABLE OF PERFECT SQUARES						
Square roots	Squares	Square roots	Squares	Square roots	Squares	
1 ⟷	1	10 ⟷	100	18 ⟷	324	This table can be read both ways and helps in positioning the decimal point when reading from mathematical tables square roots of numbers which are not perfect squares.
2	4	11	121	19	361	
3	9	12	144	20	400	
4	16	13	169	21	441	
5	25	14	196	22	484	
6	36	15	225	23	529	
7	49	16	256	24	576	
8	64	17	289	25	625	
9	81					

CHAPTER SEVENTEEN

Pythagoras' Triad

A triad of numbers is a set of three numbers related by some mathematical law. Pythagoras discovered that the lengths of the sides of a right-angled triangle were related in such a way that the sum of the squares of the lengths of the two smaller sides was always equal to the square of the length of the third and largest side. This side is always opposite the right angle and is called the hypotenuse. These sets of numbers cannot be chosen at random, because it is obvious that not every triangle contains a right angle, but by a simple calculation numbers obeying Pythagoras' triad rule can be found successfully in the following manner:

Any two numbers	2 × product	Difference of squares	Sum of squares	Triad set
2, 1	2 × 2 = 4	4 − 1 = 3	4 + 1 = 5	3, 4, 5
3, 2	2 × 6 = 12	9 − 4 = 5	9 + 4 = 13	5, 12, 13
5, 3	2 × 15 = 30	25 − 9 = 16	25 + 9 = 34	16, 30. 34
7, 11	2 × 77 = 154	121 − 49 = 72	121 + 49 = 170	72, 154, 170
16, 19	2 × 304 = 608	361 − 256 = 105	361 + 256 = 617	105, 608, 617

Geometrical Representation of Square Roots

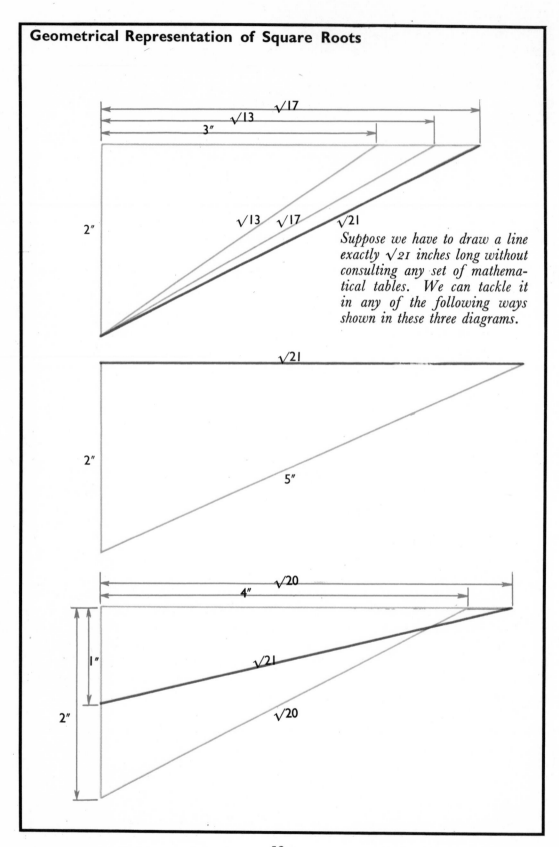

Suppose we have to draw a line exactly √21 inches long without consulting any set of mathematical tables. We can tackle it in any of the following ways shown in these three diagrams.

Proof of Pythagoras' Theorem

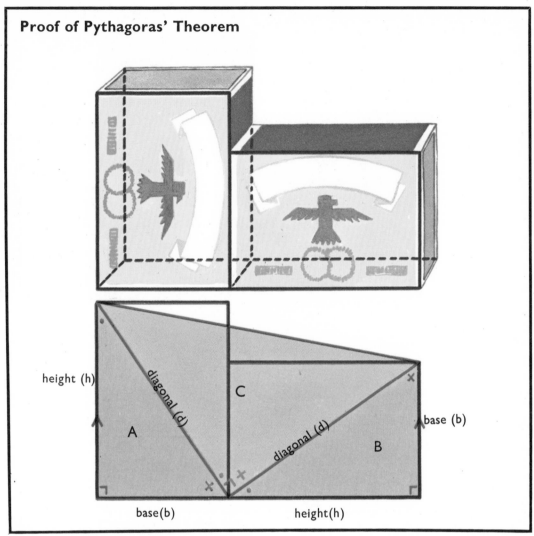

Proof. This proof starts off with facts about the area of a right-angle triangle and the area of a trapezium.

Area of trapezium = areas of triangles A + B + C

$$\frac{(\text{base} + \text{height})(\text{base} + \text{height})}{2}$$

$$= \frac{\text{base} \times \text{height}}{2} + \frac{\text{base} \times \text{height}}{2}$$

$$+ \frac{\text{diagonal} \times \text{diagonal}}{2}$$

$$\frac{(b + h)(b + h)}{2} = \frac{bh}{2} + \frac{bh}{2} + \frac{d^2}{2}$$

$$b^2 + 2bh + h^2 = bh + bh + d^2$$

$$b^2 + h^2 = d^2$$

The architects and surveyors who built the Great Pyramid at Gizeh in Egypt knew how to make a right-angle (a 90° angle) with remarkable precision. Wherever right-angles occur in the pyramid, in the sides and in the corner angles, they are correct to a fraction of a degree. The Egyptians probably achieved this accuracy by constructing right-angles with ropes and pegs. It was known that a triangle with sides 5, 4 and 3 units long is a right-angled triangle. A rope is knotted at lengths of 5, 4 and 3 units. When pegged at the knots, the rope is the outline of a right-angled triangle.

53

The Egyptians were interested in numbers, and it did not take them long to discover that the 3, 4, 5 triangle had another property. 3 × 3 (3-squared) is 9. 4 × 4 (4-squared) is 16. 5 × 5 (5-squared) is 25. And 9 + 16 = 25. Put in another way:

> The sum of squares on the two shortest sides (enclosing the right-angle), is equal to the square on the third side, the hypotenuse (opposite the right angle).

This property was also shown by other right-angled triangles in which each side was a whole number of units long. The 5, 12, 13 triangle and the 8, 15, 17 triangle are two well-known examples.

Later, around 500 B.C., the Greek mathematician Pythagoras realized that the rule applied to all right-angled triangles, and not just to special triangles with their sides whole numbers of units long.

Pythagoras' rule is a convenient way of calculating the third side of a right-

The sum of the squares on the two shortest sides is equal to the square on the hypotenuse. Below: the simplest right-angled triangle, the 3, 4, 5 triangle.

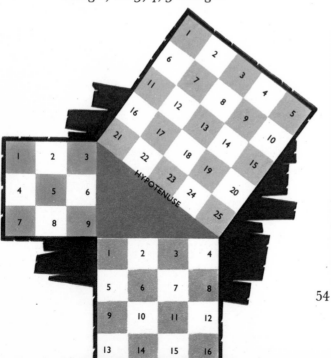

The Egyptians probably used the 3, 4, 5 triangle to construct the accurate right-angles found in the pyramids. They also knew that $3^2 + 4^2 = 5^2$, Pythagoras' theorem for this particular triangle.

angled triangle once two of the sides are known. If the lengths of the two sides enclosing the right-angle are known, the length of the hypotenuse is the *square root* of the sum of the squares of these two sides. If the hypotenuse and one of the two other sides are known, the square of the third side is the square of the hypotenuse *minus* the square of the second side.

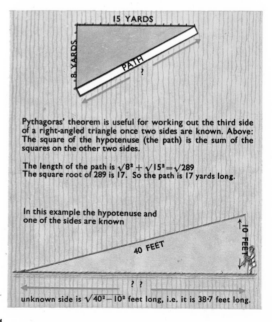

Pythagoras' theorem is useful for working out the third side of a right-angled triangle once two sides are known. Above: The square of the hypotenuse (the path) is the sum of the squares on the other two sides.

The length of the path is $\sqrt{8^2} + \sqrt{15^2} = \sqrt{289}$
The square root of 289 is 17. So the path is 17 yards long.

In this example the hypotenuse and one of the sides are known

unknown side is $\sqrt{40^2 - 10^2}$ feet long, i.e. it is 38·7 feet long.

Logarithms

CHAPTER EIGHTEEN

The Powers of Ten

FROM a knowledge of indices
$$100 = 10^1 \times 10^1 = 10^2.$$
Now if $1 \times 10^2 = 100$ what is the result of multiplying 1 by 10^{-2}? It obviously cannot be 100 because then we will be assuming that $+2$ is the same as -2 and this would cause a breakdown in the number system. We could make an intelligent guess and say that if
$$1 \times 10^2 = 100$$
then $1 \times 10^{-2} = 1 \div 10^2$
$$= 1 \times \frac{1}{10^2} = \frac{1}{100}$$

and this would mean that
$$10^{-2} = \frac{1}{10^2}.$$
This is a reasonable deduction from the argument used above. From a knowledge of indices
$$\frac{10^3}{10^5} = 10^{3-5} = 10^{-2}$$

and $\dfrac{10^3}{10^5} = \dfrac{1}{10^{5-3}} = \dfrac{1}{10^2}$

Since the same mathematical operation, that of division, has been performed with the same set of figures, the answers obtained must be equivalent. Therefore
$$10^{-2} = \frac{1}{10^2}$$

showing that the mathematical operations represented by positive indices and negative indices are *opposite in character*.

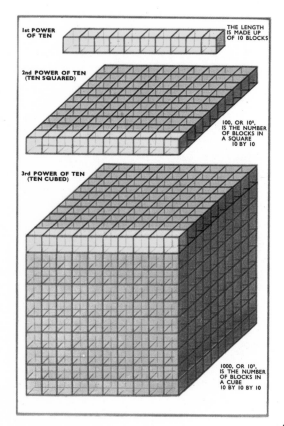

1st POWER OF TEN

THE LENGTH IS MADE UP OF 10 BLOCKS

2nd POWER OF TEN (TEN SQUARED)

100, OR 10^2, IS THE NUMBER OF BLOCKS IN A SQUARE 10 BY 10

3rd POWER OF TEN (TEN CUBED)

1000, OR 10^3, IS THE NUMBER OF BLOCKS IN A CUBE 10 BY 10 BY 10

Adding and Subtracting Negative Numbers

We are familiar with adding and subtracting positive numbers.
e.g. $(+1) + (+1) = +2.$
$(+2) - (+1) = +1.$
The latter example is very similar to
$(+2) + (-1) = +1.$

That is, *adding* a *negative* number is the same as *subtracting* a *positive* number.

But *subtracting* a *negative* number is the same as *adding* a *positive* number.

$(+2) - (-1)$ is the same as
$(+2) + (+1) = 3.$

Again $\dfrac{10^2}{10^2} = 1$

also $\dfrac{10^2}{10^2} = 10^{2-2} = 10^0$

The same mathematical operation, that of division, is performed with the same set of figures giving equivalent answers. Therefore $10^0 = 1$.

Now we have a complete range of powers of ten

$$\dots 10^{-4}, 10^{-3}, 10^{-2}, 10^{-1}, 10^0,$$
$$10^1, 10^2, 10^3, 10^4 \dots$$

in ascending order of magnitude. *When do we use this form of notation?* From a knowledge of the Universe a distant star may be 10,000,000,000, 000,000,000,000,000,000 centimetres away. At the other end of the scale, the diameter of the proton, one of the tiny building bricks of the atomic nucleus, is only about

$$\dfrac{1}{1,000,000,000,000} \text{ centimetres.}$$

This represents a vast difference in the scale of sizes of things, and the method of writing down these numbers is a rather clumsy one. A more convenient shorthand way of expressing very large and very small numbers is the *index* (plural: indices) *notation*, writing the number as a *power of ten*. The distant star is therefore 10^{28} centimetres away and the diameter of a proton 10^{-12} centimetres.

Indices need not of course be just positive or negative whole numbers. They can be fractional as well. *What do we mean when we write, for instance, $10^{\frac{1}{2}}$?*

We know that
$$10^{\frac{1}{2}} \times 10^{\frac{1}{2}} = 10^{\frac{1}{2}+\frac{1}{2}} = 10^1$$

Taking the square root of each side we have $10^{\frac{1}{2}} = \sqrt{10}$

Similarly $10^{\frac{1}{3}} \times 10^{\frac{1}{3}} \times 10^{\frac{1}{3}} = 10^1$

Taking the cube root of each side we have $10^{\frac{1}{3}} = \sqrt[3]{10}$

Yet again $10^{\frac{2}{3}} \times 10^{\frac{2}{3}} \times 10^{\frac{2}{3}} = 10^2$

Taking the cube root of each side we have $10^{\frac{2}{3}} = \sqrt[3]{10^2}$

These are equivalent forms of the same numbers known as the INDEX form and the SURD form. Converting from one form to the other is an essential manoeuvre in mathematical calculations.

Multiplication

In ordinary notation
10,000 × 100 = 1,000,000 (a million).
This can be written as
$10^4 \times 10^2 = 10^6$
The numbers can be multiplied simply by adding the two indices, or logarithms.
i.e. 10^6 is obviously 10^{4+2}.

---

100 × 1 can be written as
$10^2 \times 10^0$
Adding the logarithms, 2 and 0 gives the right answer (10^2, or 100.) The result of multiplying (or dividing) any number by one is the same number—nothing is added to (or subtracted from) the index when multiplying by one.

$10 \times \frac{1}{100}$ is written as
$10^1 \times 10^{-2}$ which is $10^{1+(-2)}$
or 10^{-1} (a tenth) the right answer.

Division

Dividing one number by another is carried out by subtracting the logarithm of one number from the other.

100,000 divided by 100 is written as
$10^5 \div 10^2$
This means 'how many times will 100 go into 100,000?' The answer is 1,000, or 10^3 which is 10^{5-2}.

---

10 divided by $\frac{1}{10}$ can be written as
$10^1 \div 10^{-1}$, or $10^{1-(-1)}$
Minus (minus one) equals plus one, so the answer is 10^2. Checking that this is the right answer: 10 divided by $\frac{1}{10}$ means 'how many tenths are there in 10?, and the answer is 100.

SURD form	INDEX form
$\sqrt[2]{10}$	$10^{\frac{1}{2}} = 10^{0.5}$
$\sqrt[3]{10}$	$10^{\frac{1}{3}} \simeq 10^{0.3333}$
$\sqrt[3]{10^2}$	$10^{\frac{2}{3}} \simeq 10^{0.6667}$
$\sqrt[5]{10^3}$	$10^{\frac{3}{5}} = 10^{0.6}$
(where $\simeq$ means 'is approximately equal to')	

The numbers in $\sqrt[2]{\ }$, $\sqrt[3]{\ }$, $\sqrt[5]{\ }$ placed over the $\sqrt{\ }$ (root) sign are called the root extraction numbers and are placed in the *denominators* of the *index fractions*, and read as the second (square), third (cube) and fifth roots of the numbers. From the index table it is easy to see that the larger the index the larger the number, and therefore in ascending order of magnitude the numbers are as follows:

$$10^{\frac{1}{2}}, \ 10^{\frac{3}{5}}, \ 10^{\frac{2}{3}}, \ 10^{\frac{3}{4}}$$

CHAPTER NINETEEN

Mapping into Logarithms

WHEN a number is expressed as a power of ten, it has a special significance for mathematical purposes. Here we have a set of numbers expressed as powers of ten.

Numbers	Powers of ten
$\frac{1}{10000}$	10^{-4}
$\frac{1}{1000}$	10^{-3}
$\frac{1}{100}$	10^{-2}
$\frac{1}{10}$	10^{-1}
1	10^0
10	10^1
100	10^2
1000	10^3
10000	10^4

Thus 100 has the equivalent index form 10^2 and $100 = 10^2$. The index 2 is called the logarithm of the number 100 using 10 as the base for equivalence.

Mathematically this is written

$$2 = \log_{10} 100$$

Continuing this argument we can say

$$\frac{1}{1000} = 10^{-3}$$

and

$$-3 = \log_{10}\left(\frac{1}{1000}\right)$$

or

$$-3 = \log_{10}(0{\cdot}001)$$

But only a very few numbers can be expressed as powers of ten in which the index is a whole number, either positive or negative. By reference to special mathematical tables (log tables) any positive number can be expressed as a power of ten.

Generally if $\mathbf{N = 10^x}$
then $\mathbf{x = \log_{10} N}$

The indices $-3, -2, -1, 0, 1, 2, 3$, etc. which can be found by inspection are called the CHARACTERISTICS of the logarithms.

	Number	Index Form	Log Characteristic
NUMBERS GREATER THAN UNITY	1000	10^3	3
	101, 102, . . . 999		between 2 and 3
	100	10^2	2
	11, 12, . . . 99		between 1 and 2
	10	10^1	1
	2, 3, . . . 9		between 0 and 1
	1	10^0	0
NUMBERS LESS THAN UNITY	0·9, 0·8, . . . 0·2		between −1 and 0
	$\frac{1}{10}$ (·1)	10^{-1}	−1
	0·09, 0·08, . . . 0·02		between −2 and −1
	$\frac{1}{100}$ (·01)	10^{-2}	−2
	0·009, 0·008, . . . 0·002		between −3 and −2
	$\frac{1}{1000}$ (·001)	10^{-3}	−3

To Find the Characteristic of a Logarithm Number

Put the number into the form $a \times 10^x$ where a is any number between 1 and 10, and x can have any integral value, positive or negative. This is called the '*standard form*' of the number because any number between 1 and 10 has the characteristic 0. Thus to find the characteristic of the number 352·4 we write the number as

$$\frac{352 \cdot 4}{100} \times 100 = 3 \cdot 524 \times 10^2.$$

The *power* or *index* of ten gives the characteristic of the equivalent log number, which in this case is 2.

Number	$a \times 10^x$ Form	Log Characteristic
5·362	$5 \cdot 362 \times 10^0$	0
536·2	$5 \cdot 362 \times 10^2$	2
0·05362	$5 \cdot 362 \times 10^{-2}$	−2
·0005362	$5 \cdot 362 \times 10^{-4}$	−4
5362000	$5 \cdot 362 \times 10^6$	6

Again

$$0.03524 = \frac{0.03524 \times 100}{100}$$

$$= \frac{3.524}{100} = 3.524 \times 10^{-2}$$

and the characteristic is -2.

As a *mnemonic*, when the number is greater than 1, the characteristic is always *one less* than the *number* of digits in the *integral* part of the number, and *positive*. When the number is *less than* 1 but greater than 0 the characteristic is *one more* than the number of noughts immediately after the decimal point, but *negative*. Therefore only numbers less than 1 but greater than 0 have *negative characteristics*.

Finding a Logarithm

Logarithmic tables vary in the way the logarithms are set out. The most usual form of 4-figure logarithmic tables (which give the mantissa or decimal part of the logarithm correct to 4 places of decimals and which are sufficiently accurate for most purposes) is set out as below.

To find, for example, log 1·145, find the first two figures in the numbers on the extreme left hand of the page. The horizontal row of figures headed by 1·1 gives all the logarithms of numbers from 1·10 to 1·19. Move along this row till the vertical column headed 4, the next figure of the number, is reached. The number in this space (0·0569) is the logarithm of 1·140. The extra bit which must be added to make up for the last figure is contained in the set of difference columns on the right-hand side of the page. The log of 1·145 is slightly bigger than the log of 1·140, the difference being under the column in the right-hand side headed '5', i.e. 19, so the log of 1·145 is

·0569 + ·0019 = ·0588.

All logarithms are found in this way, but the tables give only the mantissae. The characteristic must be determined by inspection and common sense. 1·145 is obviously between 1 and 10, so its characteristic is obviously 0. The characteristic of 11·45 (10 × 1·145) would be 1, so the logarithm would be 1·0588.

Logarithms are a very useful *mapping* of the natural numbers. Numbers can be represented by their logarithms in much the same way as a building can be represented by a black block on a map. The set of buildings is mapped to the set of blocks.

{buildings} → {black blocks}

and

{numbers} → {logarithms of the numbers}

or

Number Set	Log Set
0·001	−3
0·01	−2
0·1	−1
1·0	0
10·0	1
100·0	2
1000·0	3

Each of the numbers in the logarithm set corresponds to a *single* number in the number set. This is called *one-to-one correspondence*.

If the numbers are spaced out evenly along the number line, their corresponding logarithms will *not* be evenly spaced. If the logarithms are evenly spaced, their corresponding numbers are compressed into small unequal spacings on the number line. But, in this second case, the logarithms

	0	1	2	3	4	5	6	7	8	9	1 2 3	4 5 6	7 8 9
1·0	·0000	0043	0086	0128	0170	0212	0253	0294	0334	0374	4 8 12	17 21 25	29 33 37
1·1	·0414	0453	0492	0531	0569	0607	0645	0682	0719	0755	4 8 11	15 19 23	26 30 34
1·2	·0792	0828	0864	0899	0934	0969	1004	1038	1072	1106	3 7 10	14 17 21	24 28 31
1·3	·1139	1173	1206	1239	1271	1303	1335	1367	1399	1430	3 6 10	13 16 19	23 26 29
1·4	·1461	1492	1523	1553	1584	1614	1644	1673	1703	1732	3 6 9	12 15 18	21 24 27

FINDING A LOGARITHM

THE COLUMNS ON THE RIGHT ARE USED TO FIND THE FINAL FIGURE IN THE LOGARITHM AND ARE CALLED 'DIFFERENCE COLUMNS'

EVEN SPACING FOR NUMBERS, UNEVEN SPACING FOR LOGARITHMS – NO USE ON A SLIDE RULE

Numbers which are EVENLY spaced can be added or subtracted by moving to right or left along the number line. Here the corresponding logarithms (to base 10) take up segments of increasing size. There is no standard unit size.

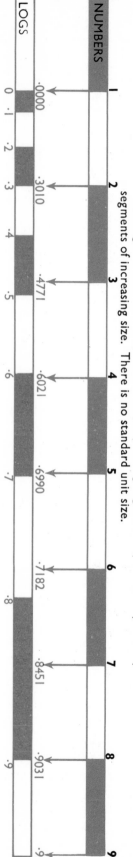

EVEN SPACING FOR LOGS – THE SLIDE RULE SCALE

The spacings on the logarithm scale are standard units. When multiplying 3 by 2 first move to the mark 3 (·4771 on log. scale), then an additional 2 units (·3010 on log. scale) to the right. In actual practice the slide rule scales are marked logarithmically with the logs of the numbers evenly spaced out but the number equivalent written down on the scale. The distance from 1 to 2 is the same as the distance from 3 to 6 on the number scale.

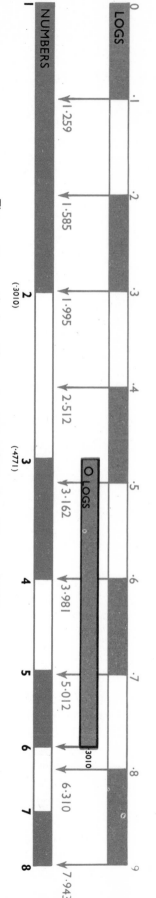

61

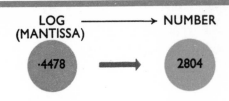

LOG ⟶ NUMBER
(MANTISSA)

·4478 ⟶ 2804

ONE-TO-ONE CORRESPONDENCE. Only one set of numbers 2804
corresponds to any one single set of numbers in the
logarithm set ?·4478. But only ONE number in the
number set corresponds to the number (0·4478) in the
logarithm set. Yet the digits 2, 8, 0 and 4 taken in that
order can represent more than one number when the position
of the decimal point is altered. How do we find the right number
from this apparent many-to-one-correspondence?

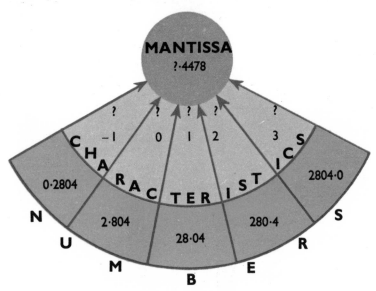

The whole number part of the logarithm number
gives the clue to the identity of the number.

can be added simply by moving along the number line. Adding a logarithm is not the same as adding its corresponding number. In the process of mapping from a number set to a logarithm set, the mathematical operations have changed. *Multiplication* in the number set has been mapped into *addition* in the logarithm set, and division has been mapped into *subtraction*. Addition and subtraction are usually much easier operations than multiplication and division. So complicated multiplication and division sums can be mapped into the set of logarithms to make the calculations easier. Then they are mapped back from the logarithm set to give the answer in terms of ordinary numbers.

Worked Examples

Multiplication

To find the number whose logarithm is 1·4478: The characteristic (the whole number part), 1 in this case, tells us that the character of the number we are looking for is such that it is a number between 10 and 100. From the logarithm tables all the numbers which have the decimal part (mantissa) ·4478 have the digits 2804 in them. The number is therefore 28·04.

Briefly the work is set out in two columns thus:

Number	Log
$7 \cdot 463 = 7 \cdot 463 \times 10^0 \rightarrow$ $\times 3 \cdot 758 = 3 \cdot 758 \times 10^0 \rightarrow$	$0 \cdot 8729$ $0 \cdot 5749 +$
N ? $2 \cdot 804 \times 10^1 \leftarrow$ $\therefore$ N $= 28 \cdot 04$	$1 \cdot 4478$

Division

To find the number whose logarithm is 0·2980: The characteristic (the whole number part), 0 in this case, tells us that the character of the number we are looking for is such that it is a single digit number between 1 and 10. From the logarithm tables all the numbers which have the decimal part (mantissa) ·2980 have the digits 1986 in them. The number is therefore 1·986.

Briefly the work is set out in two columns thus:

Number	Log
$7 \cdot 463 = 7 \cdot 463 \times 10^0 \rightarrow$ $\div 3 \cdot 758 = 3 \cdot 758 \times 10^0 \rightarrow$	$0 \cdot 8729$ $0 \cdot 5749 -$
N ? $1 \cdot 986 \times 10^0 \leftarrow$ N $= 1 \cdot 986$	$0 \cdot 2980$

Alternative Methods of Setting Out

Multiplication

$7 \cdot 463 = 10^{0 \cdot 8729}$ from statement N $= 10^x$
$\times 3 \cdot 758 = 10^{0 \cdot 5749}$

N $= 10^{0 \cdot 8729} \times 10^{0 \cdot 5749}$
    $= 10^{0 \cdot 8729 + 0 \cdot 5749}$
N $= 10^{1 \cdot 4478}$
$1 \cdot 4478 = \log_{10} N$ from statement $x = \log_{10} N$
N $= 28 \cdot 04$ (using log. tables in reverse)

Division

$7 \cdot 463 = 10^{0 \cdot 8729}$ from statement N $= 10^x$
$\div 3 \cdot 758 = 10^{0 \cdot 5749}$

N $= 10^{0 \cdot 8729} \div 10^{0 \cdot 5749}$
N $= 10^{0 \cdot 8729 - 0 \cdot 5749}$
N $= 10^{0 \cdot 2980}$
$0 \cdot 2980 = \log_{10} N$ from statement $x = \log_{10} N$
N $= 1 \cdot 986$ (using log. tables in reverse)

CHAPTER TWENTY

Using Logarithms

THE base for a logarithm can be any number. The set of powers of 2 provides such an example.

The Set of Powers of 2

Number	Index notation	Power, or log. to base 2
1	2^0	0
2	2^1	1
4	2^2	2
8	2^3	3
16	2^4	4
32	2^5	5
64	2^6	6
128	2^7	7

A very small proportion of numbers are· integral powers of 2, so using logarithms-to-the-base-two has only limited application. It is, of course, possible to base logarithm sets on the powers of three, the powers of four, the powers of five and so on. But always the usefulness of the mapping is restricted to the set of powers of each of these numbers, and the result of multiplying or dividing always belongs to this same set.

Generally

$$2 = 2^1 \text{ giving } 1 = \log_2 2$$
$$3 = 3^1 \text{ giving } 1 = \log_3 3$$
$$4 = 4^1 \text{ giving } 1 = \log_4 4$$
$$e = e^1 \text{ giving } 1 = \log_e e$$

The log of a number to its own base is always *unity*.

Using Logarithm Graphs

Graph 1. $x = 2^y$ giving $y = \log_2 x$

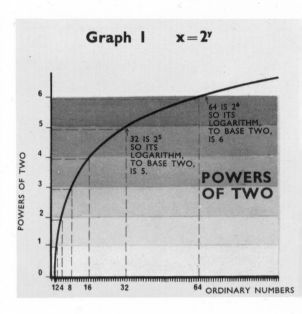

Graph 1   x = 2^y

32 IS 2^5 SO ITS LOGARITHM, TO BASE TWO, IS 5.

64 IS 2^6 SO ITS LOGARITHM, TO BASE TWO, IS 6

POWERS OF TWO

POWERS OF TWO

124 8 16   32   64   ORDINARY NUMBERS

Plot x along the horizontal axis for a range of values from $x = 1$ to $x = 64$ and $\log_2 x$ along the vertical axis. x is known as the independent variable and y as the dependent variable because the value of y becomes fixed once a value for x is chosen.

Graph 2. $x = 10^y$ giving $y = \log_{10} x$
Plot x along the horizontal axis for a range of values from $x = 1$ to $x = 100$ and $\log_{10} x$ along the vertical axis.

Graph 3. A magnified view of part of graph 2 ($x = 10^y$) is drawn, showing the curve for numbers smaller than one approaching the vertical axis but never actually meeting it.

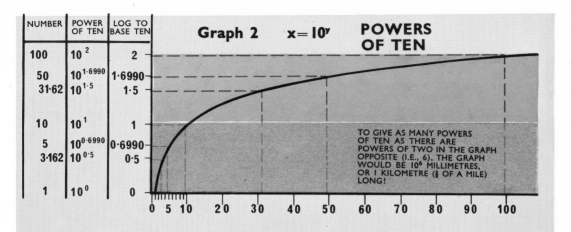

NUMBER	POWER OF TEN	LOG TO BASE TEN
100	10^2	2
50	$10^{1 \cdot 6990}$	$1 \cdot 6990$
31·62	$10^{1 \cdot 5}$	$1 \cdot 5$
10	10^1	1
5	$10^{0 \cdot 6990}$	$0 \cdot 6990$
3·162	$10^{0 \cdot 5}$	$0 \cdot 5$
1	10^0	0

Graph 2 $x = 10^y$ **POWERS OF TEN**

TO GIVE AS MANY POWERS OF TEN AS THERE ARE POWERS OF TWO IN THE GRAPH OPPOSITE (I.E., 6), THE GRAPH WOULD BE 10^6 MILLIMETRES, OR 1 KILOMETRE (⅝ OF A MILE) LONG!

Ordinary logarithms are called logarithms *to the base* 10 because the logs are the powers of ten. 100 is 10^2 and log 100 is 2. But any number can be used as a base of a system of logs. 2 is the base of binary logarithms. 8 is 2^3, so the log of 8, *to the base* 2, is 3.

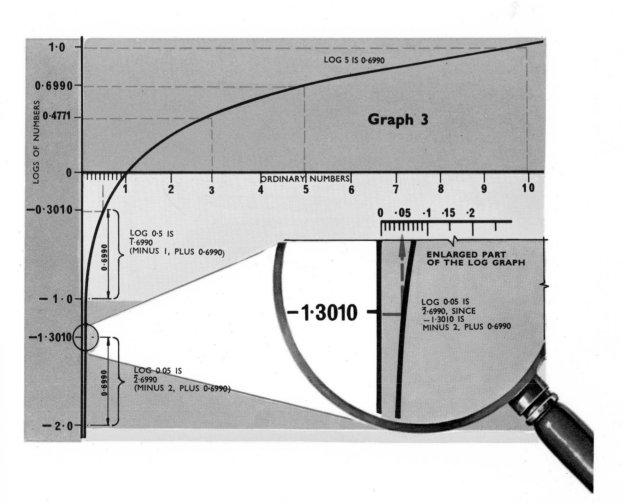

LOGS OF NUMBERS

LOG 5 IS 0·6990

Graph 3

ORDINARY NUMBERS

LOG 0·5 IS
$\bar{1}$·6990
(MINUS 1, PLUS 0·6990)

0·6990

ENLARGED PART OF THE LOG GRAPH

−1·3010

LOG 0·05 IS
$\bar{2}$·6990, SINCE
−1·3010 IS
MINUS 2, PLUS 0·6990

LOG 0·05 IS
$\bar{2}$·6990
(MINUS 2, PLUS 0·6990)

0·6990

$$4 \times 16 \leftrightarrow 2^2 \times 2^4 = 2^6 = 64 \qquad \text{therefore}$$
$$\log_2 4 + \log_2 16 \leftrightarrow 2 + 4 = 6 = \log_2 64$$

$\times \rightarrow +$

$$64 \div 32 \leftrightarrow 2^6 \div 2^5 = 2^1 = 2 \qquad \text{therefore}$$
$$\log_2 64 - \log_2 32 \leftrightarrow 6 - 5 = 1 = \log_2 2$$

$\div \rightarrow -$

Adding the indices (the logarithms) is the same as multiplying the numbers. Subtracting the indices is equivalent to division. But the method works only when the numbers to be multiplied or divided belong to the set of powers of the same number.

To simplify the situation, practical logarithms are based on ten. The use of logarithms makes multiplication and division, and a host of other arithmetic processes, easier by converting multiplication into an addition process and division into subtraction.

Logarithm Numbers

Numbers can be expressed in two ways:

(i) wholly positive, e.g. 2·546, and
(ii) wholly negative, e.g. —2·546.

Although logarithm numbers may be expressed as wholly positive numbers they cannot be expressed as wholly negative numbers. They are expressed in a form that is partly negative and partly positive; the *integral* part being *negative* and the *decimal* part *positive*. Thus $-2\cdot546$ is written as $\bar{3}\cdot454$ obtained as shown below.

To distinguish between the minus 3 and the plus 0·454 the number is written $\bar{3}\cdot454$ with the minus sign written *above* the 3 and the number is read as bar 3 decimal 454.

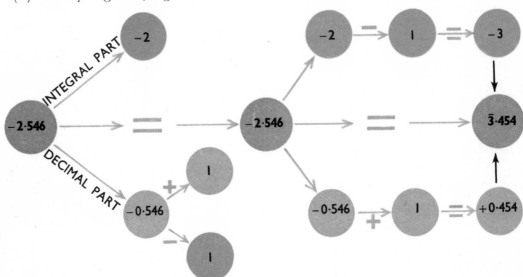

Numbers Smaller than One

Multiplying and dividing with numbers smaller than one requires mapping into logarithms with negative characteristics, which necessitates addition and subtraction in mixed numbers.

Example

$$0.3462 \times 0.07653$$

Briefly the work is set out in two columns thus:

Number	←→	Log
$0.3462 = 3.462 \times 10^{1}$	←→	$\overline{1}.5394$
$\times 0.07653 = 7.653 \times 10^{2}$	←→	$\overline{2}.8839 +$
	N?←→	$\overline{2}.4233$
2.651×10^{-2}		(Adding the whole numbers algebraically we have $-1-2+1=-2$.)
0.02651		

The same two numbers divided:

$$0.3462 \div 0.07653$$

Number	Log
$0.3462 = 3.462 \times 10^{-1}$	$\overline{1}.5394 + 1 - 1$
$\div 0.07653 = 7.653 \times 10^{-2}$	$\overline{2}.8839 -$
$N = ?$	0.6555
4.525×10^{0}	(Subtracting the whole numbers algebraically
4.524	$-1-1-(-2)$
	$= -2 + 2 = 0$)

Multiplying Numbers Smaller than One

When multiplying by a number smaller than 1, the mantissa must be treated as a positive number and the characteristic as a negative number; e.g. to find 1.145×0.0543

The log $(1.145 \times 0.0543) = \log 1.145 + \log 0.0543$
Log 1.145 is 0.0588. To find log of 0.0543 (i.e. 5.43×10^{-2}) the characteristic of the log is $\overline{2}$.

The mantissa is found by looking up log 5.43. This is 0.7348, so log 0.0543 is $\overline{2}.7348$. So log (1.145×0.0543) is $0.0588 + \overline{2}.7348 = \overline{2}.7936$. The antilog of this is $6.218 \times 10^{-2} = 0.06218$.

Dividing with Logarithms

Division using positive logarithms (logarithms of numbers greater than 1) is similar to multiplication, except that the log of the number dividing the other number is subtracted from it instead of being added to it.

The answer may be a negative logarithm:
e.g. the log of 2.5 is 0.3979
the log of 56.2 is 1.7497
log $(2.5 \div 56.2)$ is log $\overline{2.5} - \log$ of $56.2 = \overline{2}.6482$
Once again, the antilog of the mantissa, 0.6482, is looked up in the table and found to be 4.448. Because the characteristic is $\overline{2}$ the answer is 0.04448 (4.448×10^{-2})

When dividing by a number smaller than 1, it must be remembered that the characteristic only of this number is negative:
e.g. $2.5 \div 0.00095$
log of 2.5 is 0.3979
log 0.00095 is $\overline{4}.9777$
log $(2.5 \div 0.00095)$ is $\overline{3.4202}$
and the antilog of 3.4202 is 2631, the answer.

Multiplication Using Log Tables

To multiply two numbers, simply find the logarithms of the two numbers from the tables, and add them:
e.g. to find 1.145×87.56
The log of 1.145 is 0.0588
The log of 87.56 is $1.9420 + 0.0003 = 1.9423$
so the log of (1.145×87.56) is
log of $1.145 +$ log of 87.56
$= 0.0588 + 1.9423 = \overline{2.0011}$

The problem is $\overline{\text{now}}$ to find the number whose logarithm is 2.0011. The characteristic, 2, is ignored at first because it simply tells the position of the decimal point in the answer. The problem is to find the number which the mantissa $.0011$ represents (its *antilog*). Looking at the log table it is obvious that it is less than $.0043$, the second mantissa in the first row of the table, but greater than $.0000$, the first mantissa in the first row of the table. The mantissa is in fact $.0011$ greater than $.0000$.

Looking along the first row to the 'difference' columns at the right-hand side, it will be seen that the number shown nearest to 11 is 12. This is in the '3' difference column and gives us the fourth figure. So the number represented by the mantissa $.0011$ is 1.003. The characteristic of the logarithm is 2. The answer is therefore 100.3 (1.003×10^{2})

	0	1	2	3	4	5	6	7	8	9	1	2	3	4	5	6	7	8	9
8·5	·9294	9299	9304	9309	9315	9320	9325	9330	9335	9340	1	1	2	2	3	3	4	4	5
8·6	·9345	9350	9355	9360	9365	9370	9375	9380	9385	9390	1	1	2	2	3	3	4	4	5
8·7	·9395	9400	9405	9410	9415	9420	9425	9430	9435	9440	0	1	1	2	2	3	3	4	4
8·8	·9445	9450	9455	9460	9465	9469	9474	9479	9484	9489	0	1	1	2	2	3	3	4	4
8·9	·9494	9499	9504	9509	9513	9518	9523	9528	9533	9538	0	1	1	2	2	3	3	4	4

	0	1	2	3	4	5	6	7	8	9	1	2	3	4	5	6	7	8	9
1·0	·0000	0043	0086	0128	0170	0212	0253	0294	0334	0374	4	8	12	17	21	25	29	33	37
1·1	·0414	0453	0492	0531	0569	0607	0645	0682	0719	0755	4	8	11	15	19	23	26	30	34
1·2	·0792	0828	0864	0899	0934	0969	1004	1038	1072	1106	3	7	10	14	17	21	24	28	31
1·3	·1139	1173	1206	1239	1271	1303	1335	1367	1399	1430	3	6	10	13	16	19	23	26	29
1·4	·1461	1492	1523	1553	1584	1614	1644	1673	1703	1732	3	6	9	12	15	18	21	24	27

CHAPTER TWENTY-ONE

Application of Logarithms

USING a slide rule is a quick and convenient method of multiplying or dividing numbers, while getting a reasonably accurate result. The slide rule may have many different scales for specialized purposes, but for multiplying and dividing any numbers, only two of these scales are really necessary. These are usually labelled C and D. The D-scale is on the main body of the rule, while the C-scale is the lower scale on the sliding strip.

On an ordinary ruler scale the units are equally spaced. Because the units are equally spaced, two rulers can form a simple slide rule capable of addition and subtraction. But the units on the C- and D-scales of a slide rule are not equally spaced. The distance between '2' and '3', for example, on these scales is longer than the distance between '3' and '4'. They are, in fact, *logarithmic* scales.

The numbers on the scales are unequally spaced so that their *logarithms are equally spaced*. The numbers on the scale range from 1 to 10. Their corresponding logarithms (which can easily be verified from log tables) range from 0·0 to 1·0.

The spacings on the corresponding logarithmic scales are similar to the spacings on an ordinary ruler, i.e. equally spaced, and, like two rulers, two log scales on scales sliding alongside each other can be used for adding and subtracting the logarithms.

Adding the logarithms of any numbers has the same result as multiplying the numbers themselves. Subtracting one logarithm from another produces the same result as division of the numbers. The procedure in multiplying and dividing using log tables is first to look up the logarithms of the numbers, add or subtract as required, then look up the antilogarithm (the number corresponding to the given logarithm) of the result.

On a slide rule there is no need to look up logarithms or anti-logarithms. This has already been allowed for in arranging the numbers on the C- and D-scales in their particular way. For

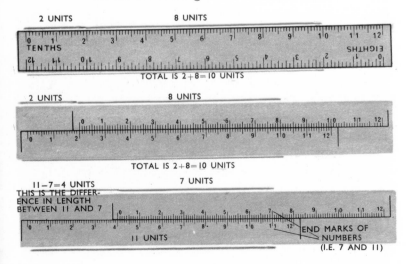

An ordinary ruler being used to add two numbers. Add 2 by moving 2 units along. Add 8: move another 8 along to arrive at the sum, i.e. 10.

This is a lot easier if two rulers are used (using, of course, two adjacent inch scales). One ruler represents one number, and the other ruler the other number. The rulers form a kind of slide rule.

The two rulers can be used to subtract numbers. The 'end' marks off two numbers, i.e. 7 and 11 are lined up, and the answer is read off as the point on one scale where the zero mark of the other cuts it, i.e. 4.

Multiplication

COPYRIGHT

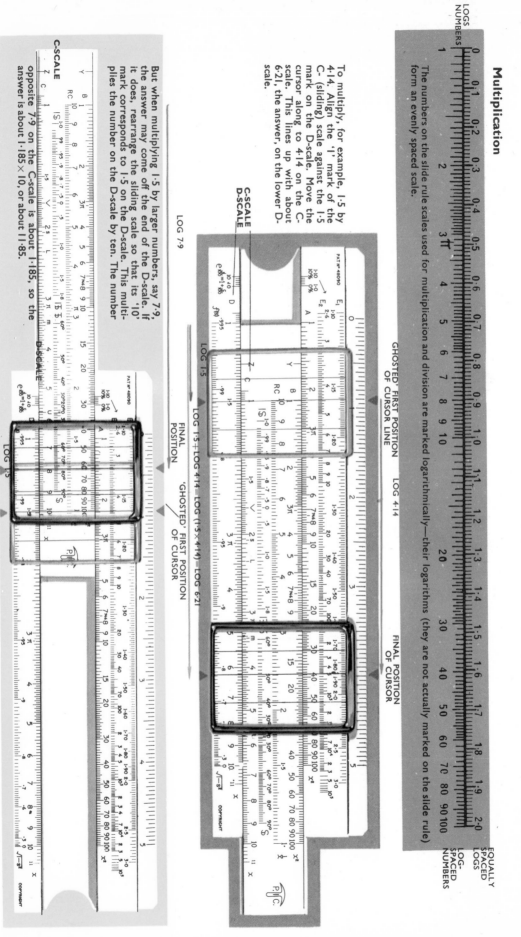

The numbers on the slide rule scales used for multiplication and division are marked logarithmically—their logarithms (they are not actually marked on the slide rule) form an evenly spaced scale.

To multiply, for example, 1·5 by 4·14. Align the '1' mark of the C- (sliding) scale against the 1·5 mark on the D-scale. Move the cursor along to 4·14 on the C-scale. This lines up with about 6·21, the answer, on the lower D-scale.

But when multiplying 1·5 by larger numbers, say 7·9, the answer may come off the end of the D-scale. If it does, rearrange the sliding scale so that its '10' mark corresponds to 1·5 on the D-scale. This multiplies the number on the D-scale by ten.

Opposite 7·9 on the C-scale is about 1·185, so the answer is about 1·185 × 10, or about 11·85.

LOG 1·5 + LOG 7·9 = LOG (1·5 × 7·9) = LOG 11·85

LOG 1·5 + LOG 4·14 = LOG (1·5 × 4·14) = LOG 6·21

'GHOSTED' FIRST POSITION OF CURSOR LINE

LOG 1·5

LOG 4·14

FINAL POSITION OF CURSOR

LOG 7·9

LOG 1·5

FINAL POSITION

'GHOSTED' FIRST POSITION OF CURSOR

C-SCALE
D-SCALE

C-SCALE
D-SCALE

LOGS
NUMBERS

EQUALLY SPACED LOGS

LOG-SPACED NUMBERS

Division

One number is subtracted from another by sliding the rulers to place the numbers side by side, and comparing their lengths. The difference in length is the answer. Similarly, the lengths corresponding to the logarithms of two numbers are compared, and the difference between them is the result of dividing one by the other.

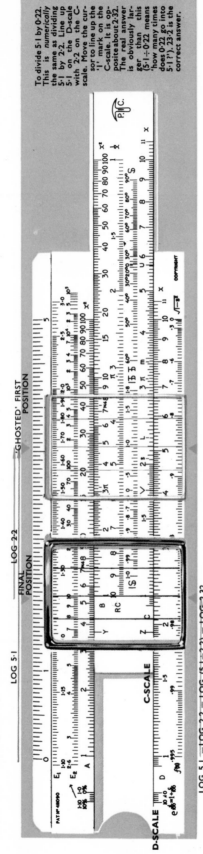

LOG 5·1

LOG 2·2

'GHOSTED' FIRST POSITION

FINAL POSITION

To divide 5·1 by 0·22. This is numerically the same as dividing 5·1 by 2·2. Line up 5·1 on the D-scale with 2·2 on the C-scale. Move the cursor to line up the '1' mark on the C-scale. It is opposite about 2·32. The real answer is obviously larger than this (5·1÷0·22 means 'how many times does 0·22 go into 5·1?'), 23·2 is the correct answer.

LOG 5.1 − LOG 2.2 = LOG (5.1÷2.2) = LOG 2.32

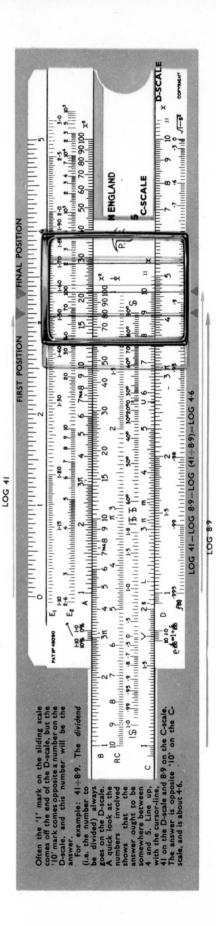

LOG 41

FIRST POSITION

FINAL POSITION

Often the '1' mark on the sliding scale comes off the end of the D-scale, but the '10' mark comes opposite a number on the D-scale, and this number will be the answer.

For example: 41÷8·9. The dividend (i.e. the number to be divided) always goes on the D-scale. A quick look at the numbers involved shows that the answer ought to be somewhere between 4 and 5. Line up, with the cursor-line, 41 on the D-scale and 8·9 on the C-scale. The answer is opposite '10' on the C-scale, and is about 4·6.

LOG 41 − LOG 8·9 = LOG (41÷8·9) = LOG 4·6

LOG 8·9

Position of the Decimal Point

The slide rule gives the right figures of the answer, but not the position of the decimal point. This can be worked out by common sense. Alternatively, there is a simple rule-of-thumb method.

When multiplying add together the numbers of figures in front of the decimal point in each number. If the end of the sliding scale is out to the left of the rule, this sum is the number of figures in front of the decimal point in the answer. However, if the sliding scale comes out to the right, subtract one.

When dividing, subtract the number of figures in the underneath number (the *divisor*) from the number on top. This gives the number of figures in the answer if the sliding scale remains to the left, but if it appears to the right, add one.

Number	No. of Figures
690·3	3
69·03	2
6·903	1
0·6903	0
0·06903	—1
0·006903	—2

This table indicates the no. of figures for this purpose

N.B. If the number is less than one then count the number of noughts immediately after the decimal point, and treat them as minus numbers.

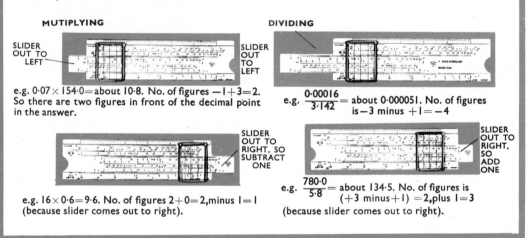

MUTIPLYING

SLIDER OUT TO LEFT

SLIDER OUT TO LEFT

e.g. 0·07 × 154·0 = about 10·8. No. of figures —1+3=2. So there are two figures in front of the decimal point in the answer.

DIVIDING

e.g. $\frac{0·00016}{3·142}$ = about 0·000051. No. of figures is —3 minus +1 = —4

SLIDER OUT TO RIGHT, SO SUBTRACT ONE

e.g. 16 × 0·6 = 9·6. No. of figures 2+0=2, minus 1=1 (because slider comes out to right).

SLIDER OUT TO RIGHT, SO ADD ONE

e.g. $\frac{780·0}{5·8}$ = about 134·5. No. of figures is (+3 minus +1) =2, plus 1=3 (because slider comes out to right).

instance, '3' on either of these scales is marked at 0·4771 (i.e. log 3) of the length of the scale. Multiplying by 3 will mean adding the *length* 0·4771. Numbers are multiplied (and logarithms added) by sliding one scale alongside the other, using the transparent *cursor* to line up markings more exactly.

Ordinary slide rules are nowhere near as accurate as 4-figure log tables. The accuracy depends simply on how accurate the user is in judging a fraction of a scale division. The longer the slide rule, the more accurate the results it is capable of giving, as all the scale divisions are larger.

Patient's temperature (along the vertical axis) is being plotted against time (along the horizontal axis). It is unnecessary to start the temperature scale at zero, for the patient's temperature will never drop as low as that.

Graphical Work

CHAPTER TWENTY-TWO

Loci

THE path traced out by a point moving under a fixed condition, or fixed set of conditions, is called its LOCUS.

Some Simple Loci

A point moves so that it is always equidistant from two fixed points. The locus (or path) traced out by the moving point is the perpendicular

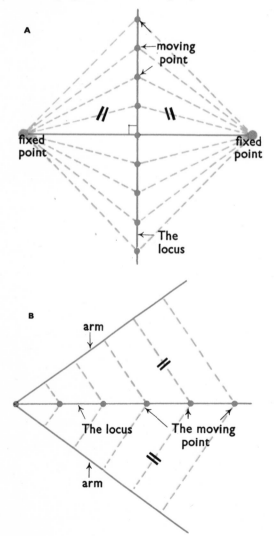

bisector of the line joining the two fixed points.

A point moves so that it is equidistant from the arms of an angle. The locus is the bisector of the angle.

A point moves so that it is always equidistant from a fixed point. The locus is the perimeter of a circle, the name given to the area enclosed. The fixed point is its centre and the constant distance the radius.

A point moves so that its distance from a *fixed point* is always equal to its distance from a *fixed straight line*. The locus is a PARABOLA, the fixed point the *focus* and the fixed straight line the *directrix*.

The ratio of the distance of the moving point from the fixed point to the distance of the moving point from the fixed straight line is called the *eccentricity* (e).

When e = 1 the locus is a PARABOLA.
When e < 1 the locus is an ELLIPSE.
When e > 1 the locus is a HYPERBOLA.

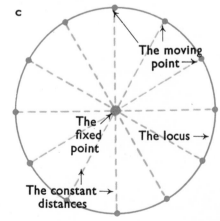

74

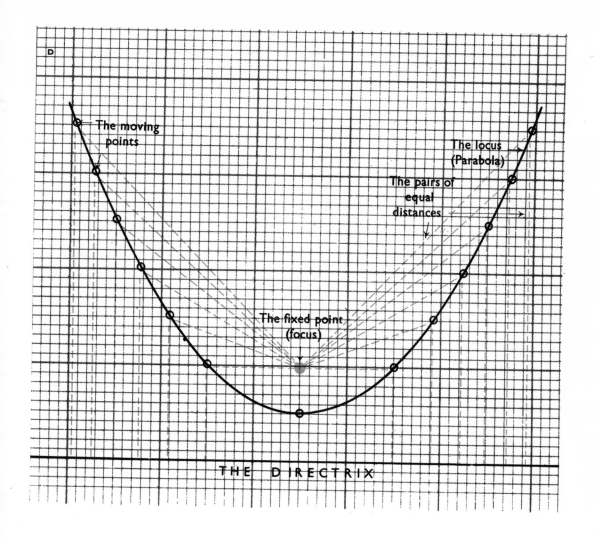

D

The moving
points

The locus
(Parabola)

The pairs of
equal
distances

The fixed point
(focus)

THE DIRECTRIX

A coin (circle) rolls along a straight line, without slipping, and a point on its circumference traces out a path. The locus is a CYCLOID.

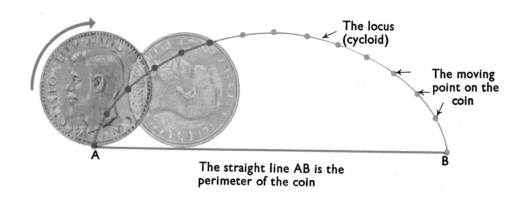

E

The locus
(cycloid)

The moving
point on the
coin

A

B

The straight line AB is the
perimeter of the coin

75

THE CONE AND ITS FAMILY OF CURVES

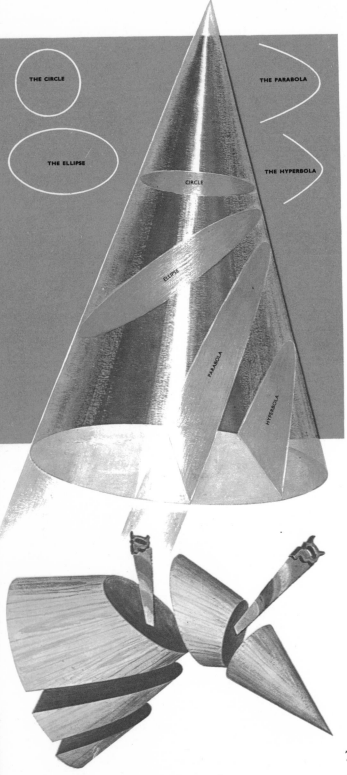

THE CIRCLE

THE ELLIPSE

THE PARABOLA

THE HYPERBOLA

CIRCLE

ELLIPSE

PARABOLA

HYPERBOLA

CONSTANT RADIUS

The slope at various points on a circumference of a circle is not constant. However the radius is the same for all points on the circle.

THE least complicated shapes which lines can take are the *straight line*, the *circle*, the *ellipse*, the *parabola* and the *hyperbola*. They are all smooth lines with no odd bumps in them. Although they look dissimilar, these lines have several properties in common. One of the properties is their origin, the *cone*.

It is not difficult to construct the straight line (with a ruler) or the circle (with a pair of compasses). The ellipse,

The tension in the string keeps the ball moving on a circle. Gravitational and electrical forces may also cause circular orbits.

76

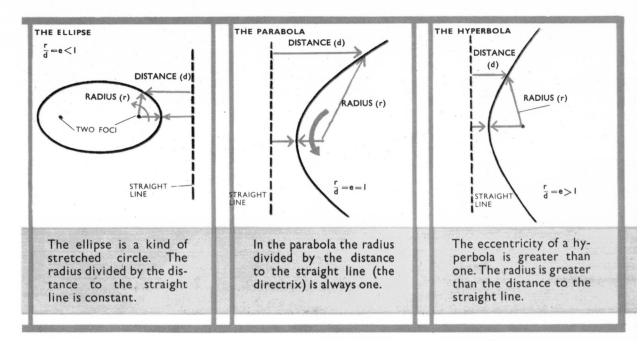

THE ELLIPSE

$\frac{r}{d} = e < 1$

DISTANCE (d)

RADIUS (r)

TWO FOCI

STRAIGHT LINE

The ellipse is a kind of stretched circle. The radius divided by the distance to the straight line is constant.

THE PARABOLA

DISTANCE (d)

RADIUS (r)

STRAIGHT LINE

$\frac{r}{d} = e = 1$

In the parabola the radius divided by the distance to the straight line (the directrix) is always one.

THE HYPERBOLA

DISTANCE (d)

RADIUS (r)

STRAIGHT LINE

$\frac{r}{d} = e > 1$

The eccentricity of a hyperbola is greater than one. The radius is greater than the distance to the straight line.

the parabola and the hyperbola require a little more guile. But these shapes can be easily obtained from the cone. In fact, every single variety can be discovered by chopping up a wooden cone.

The *straight line* is the sloping side of the cone. Any cut parallel to the circular base of the cone reveals a *circle*. Sloping cuts give the two cut surfaces the shape of an *ellipse*, provided that both ends of the cut go through the sloping sides.

The cut which is parallel to the other sloping side, opens up a parabola. The final shape, the *hyperbola*, follows on from the parabola. The cut starts on one sloping side and finishes in the base. But the cut is more nearly vertical than it is for the parabola.

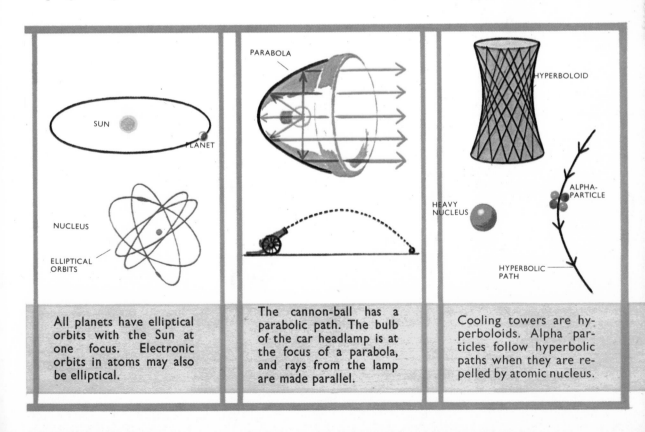

SUN

PLANET

NUCLEUS

ELLIPTICAL ORBITS

PARABOLA

HEAVY NUCLEUS

HYPERBOLOID

ALPHA-PARTICLE

HYPERBOLIC PATH

All planets have elliptical orbits with the Sun at one focus. Electronic orbits in atoms may also be elliptical.

The cannon-ball has a parabolic path. The bulb of the car headlamp is at the focus of a parabola, and rays from the lamp are made parallel.

Cooling towers are hyperboloids. Alpha particles follow hyperbolic paths when they are repelled by atomic nucleus.

CHAPTER TWENTY-THREE

Introduction to Graphs

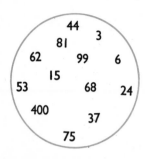

HERE we have a random selection of numbers in disarray. This arrangement serves no other purpose than to confuse. A tidying-up process can be done in several ways. The numbers could be arranged in a straight line in either ascending or descending order of magnitude as follows:

ascending
────────────────→
3, 6, 15, 24, 37, 44, 53, 62, 68, 75, 81, 99, 400
←──────────────── descending

An improved arrangement could be

3, 15, 37, 53, 75, 81, 99 odd numbers
6, 24, 44, 62, 68, 400 even numbers

A haphazard arrangement which could lead to a miscalculation

or yet again clockwise (above).

In each case it is easier to pick out any particular number required when the arrangement is systematic. The advantage gained is one of visual impression. Books in a library are catalogued and arranged to create a visual picture for quick reference. Filing systems for documents and the monumental task of recording births, fingerprints, etc., have all evolved from this practice of creating a helpful visual impression. In a game of bridge the thirteen cards can be arranged so that there is no confusion between the black cards and the red cards, and their respective values.

A better arrangement with the same set of cards.

A day in the life of a child

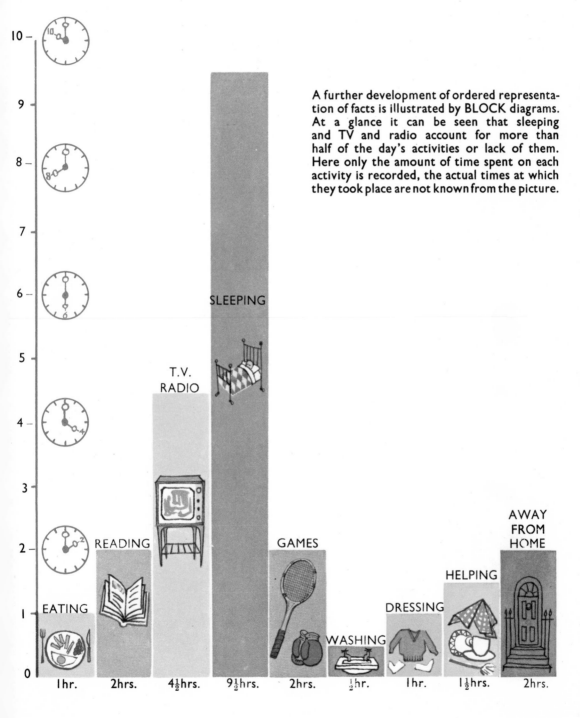

A further development of ordered representation of facts is illustrated by BLOCK diagrams. At a glance it can be seen that sleeping and TV and radio account for more than half of the day's activities or lack of them. Here only the amount of time spent on each activity is recorded, the actual times at which they took place are not known from the picture.

EATING   1hr.
READING   2hrs.
T.V. RADIO   4½hrs.
SLEEPING   9½hrs.
GAMES   2hrs.
WASHING   ½hr.
DRESSING   1hr.
HELPING   1½hrs.
AWAY FROM HOME   2hrs.

Plotting of Points

There are three generally accepted ways of fixing the position of a point in a plane:

   (i) Two lines intersecting.
  (ii) A line cutting across an arc.
(iii) Two arcs intersecting.

Two lines intersecting fixing the position of a point.

An arc and a straight line fixing the position of a point.

Two intersecting arcs fixing the position of a point.

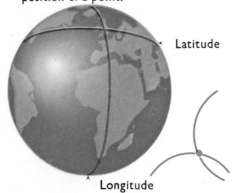

Latitude

Longitude

Descartes first showed how to position a point on ordinary flat graph paper. Two straight lines at right angles were used as base lines, the one horizontal and the other vertical. They were called the axes. Where the axes intersect is called the origin or the starting point of the measurements. Distances measured *above* the *horizontal* lines are *positive* distances, *below* the line are *negative*. Distances measured to the *right* of the *vertical* line are *positive* distances, to the *left* are *negative*. A point is represented thus: (x, y) where x is the distance along the x-axis and y is the distance along the y-axis; x and y are known as Cartesian co-ordinates.

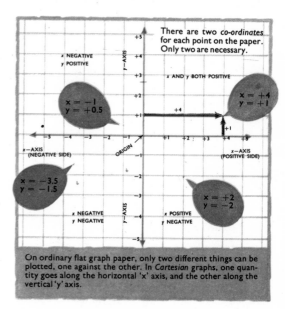

On ordinary flat graph paper, only two different things can be plotted, one against the other. In *Cartesian* graphs, one quantity goes along the horizontal 'x' axis, and the other along the vertical 'y' axis.

A second method of positioning a point on a flat piece of paper is by turning through a +ve angle from a given position on an initial line and then measuring the required distance along the arm of this angle. The point is represented thus (r, θ) which are called the polar co-ordinates of the point.

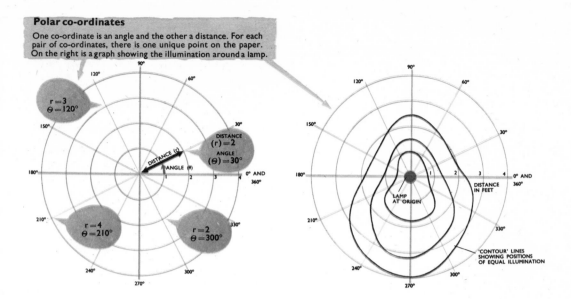

Polar co-ordinates

One co-ordinate is an angle and the other a distance. For each
pair of co-ordinates, there is one unique point on the paper.
On the right is a graph showing the illumination around a lamp.

The Straight Line

The distance of the point P on the
straight line from the x-axis is denoted
by the ordinate value *y* and is made
up of two parts – the blue line plus
the red line. The red line is the same
for each position of P and the ratio of
the length of the blue line to the
corresponding *x* value is constant.
By similar triangles:

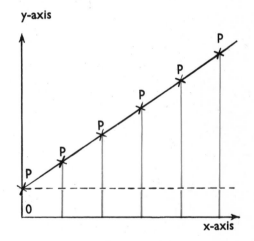

$$\frac{\text{blue line}}{x \text{ co-ordinate}} = \text{constant } (m)$$

∴ blue line = *x* co-ordinate ×
constant.

i.e.   *y* = blue line + red line

∴   *y* = *x* × constant (*m*) + a
different constant (*c*)

y = *mx* + *c*

where   *m* = gradient constant

and   *c* = intercept constant

An examination of this result

$$y = mx + c$$

shows that when *c* = 0 the line goes
through the origin, and when the
slope is nil the line is *horizontal* and
parallel to the x-axis and therefore
y = *c*; when the line makes an angle
of 90° with the x-axis the line is
vertical and *parallel* to the y-axis and
therefore *x* = *k*, a different constant.

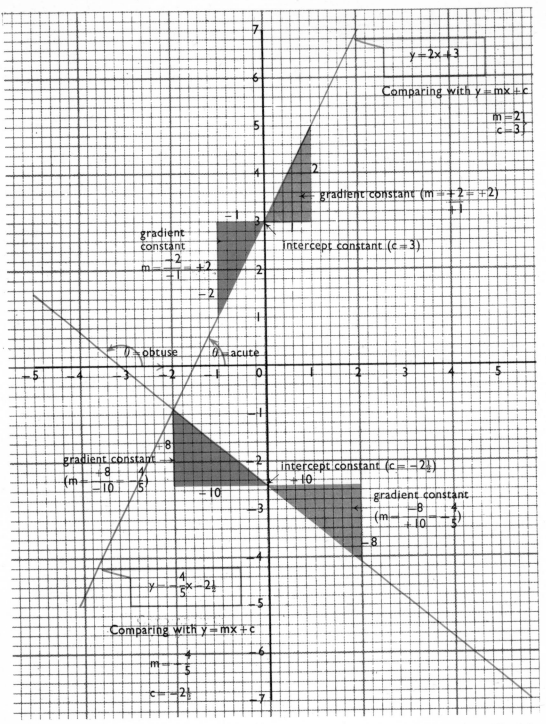

It is only necessary to plot three points to fix the position of the straight line. When the coefficient of x is +ve then the angle the straight line makes with the +ve direction of the x-axis is acute (less than 90°); when the coefficient of x is —ve then the angle the straight line makes with the +ve direction of the x-axis is obtuse (greater than 90°). The slope is always the same and the intercept constant plotted first; then from this point the gradient is measured as in the two diagrams.

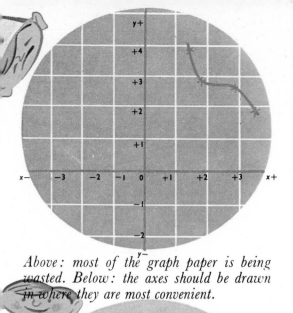

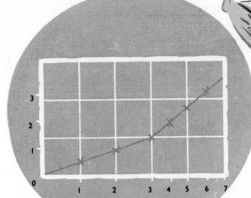

Above: most of the graph paper is being wasted. Below: the axes should be drawn in where they are most convenient.

Above: Scales should not change half-way. Otherwise an odd bend may result. Below: The units on the scale should be easy to use, and the scale written down somewhere on the paper.

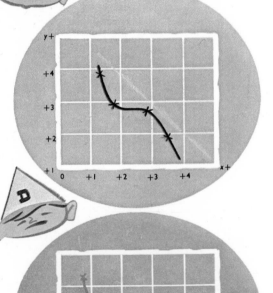

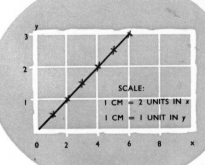

SCALE:

1 CM = 2 UNITS IN x

1 CM = 1 UNIT IN y

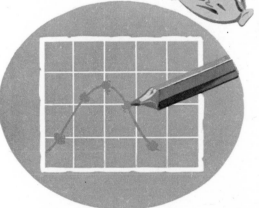

Above: Points obviously lying on a curve should not be joined with straight lines. Below: They should be joined to form a smooth curve.

Above: Points should not be marked with large messy splodges. Below: They should be marked with a sharp pencil, preferably with a cross.

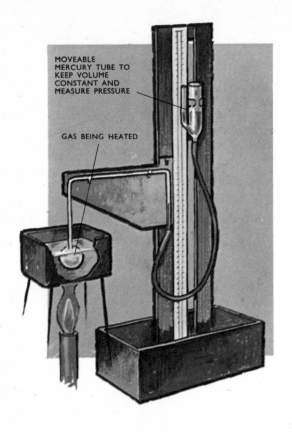

MOVEABLE MERCURY TUBE TO KEEP VOLUME CONSTANT AND MEASURE PRESSURE

GAS BEING HEATED

Heating a gas at constant volume

Temperature (in °C)	Pressure (in cm Hg)
0°	54·2
20°	55·5
40°	59·0
60°	63·6
80°	67·1
100°	70·5

When a gas is heated, both its pressure and volume normally alter. So in this experiment, volume is kept constant, while the pressure and temperature vary.

A graph is often the most convenient way of showing how things vary. For instance, patients' temperatures are plotted at regular intervals in hospitals on graphs with temperature along one axis (usually the vertical

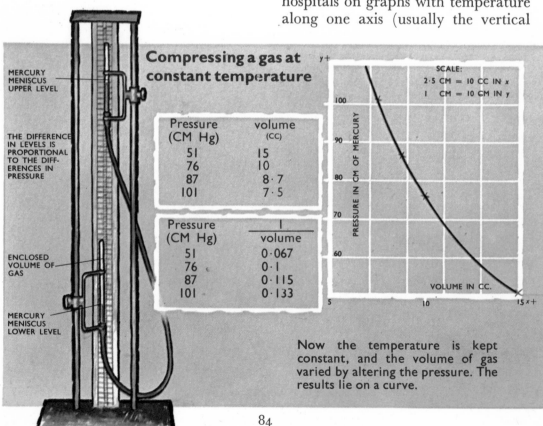

MERCURY MENISCUS UPPER LEVEL

THE DIFFERENCE IN LEVELS IS PROPORTIONAL TO THE DIFFERENCES IN PRESSURE

ENCLOSED VOLUME OF GAS

MERCURY MENISCUS LOWER LEVEL

Compressing a gas at constant temperature

Pressure (CM Hg)	volume (CC)
51	15
76	10
87	8·7
101	7·5

Pressure (CM Hg)	$\dfrac{1}{volume}$
51	0·067
76	0·1
87	0·115
101	0·133

SCALE:
2·5 CM = 10 CC IN x
1 CM = 10 CM IN y

PRESSURE IN CM OF MERCURY

VOLUME IN CC.

Now the temperature is kept constant, and the volume of gas varied by altering the pressure. The results lie on a curve.

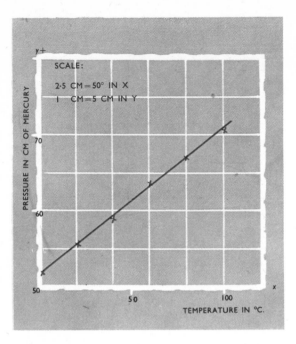

one) and time along the other axis. It is far easier for the doctor to see how the temperature is varying from a graph than it would be if he were presented with a table of figures.

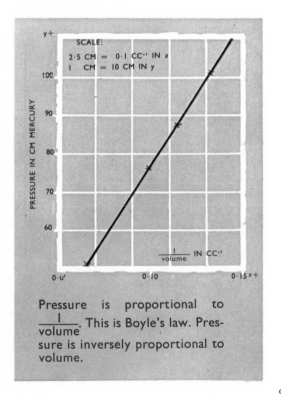

Pressure is proportional to $\frac{1}{\text{volume}}$. This is Boyle's law. Pressure is inversely proportional to volume.

When the temperature of a gas is varied in a laboratory experiment, it is found that the pressure and volume of the gas varies too. The ordinary graph cannot cope with three varying quantities at the same time, so the usual procedure is to keep one of them (e.g. the volume) exactly the same while the other two (the pressure and the temperature) are being investigated.

If a gas like hydrogen or helium is being heated, and at each different temperature the pressure is measured, the results, plotted on a graph, should lie on a straight line. When this happens the pressure is *directly proportional* to the temperature.

In another similar experiment, the temperature is kept exactly the same throughout the experiment. The two other quantities, volume and pressure, are plotted against each other on a graph; the results will lie on a curve.

Pressure is obviously not directly proportional to volume. In the experiment, it would be found that the volume actually decreased as the pressure increased. This gives a clue that pressure might be proportional to $\frac{1}{\text{volume}}$, or *inversely proportional* to the volume. It is easy to see if this is so by plotting the results on a graph, with pressure along one axis and $\frac{1}{\text{volume}}$ along the other axis, for the readings do then lie on a straight line.

Graphs have many other important uses. Two things that can be found directly from the graph are the 'area under the graph' and the slope, or *gradient*, of the graph. Both these are important in the branch of Mathematics called *calculus*.

CHAPTER TWENTY-FOUR

The Gradient of a Curve

THE slope, or gradient, of a road need not be known very precisely, and it is most easily measured by finding the increase in height corresponding to a certain distance along the slope. A road sign saying 'Steep Hill, 1 in 5' implies that for every five feet a car goes along the road, it goes up (vertically) one foot. These two distances are two of the sides of a right-angled triangle. The distance moved vertically is the vertical side of the triangle and the distance along the slope, the sloping side, or hypotenuse. The gradient of the road is the rate of change of height with distance.

However, in mathematics, gradients are measured in a different way. The same right-angled triangle is used, but instead of involving the sloping side, the gradient is found by dividing the two other sides. The gradient is equal to the length of the vertical side divided by the length of the horizontal side.

Gradients are important in mathematics since they show rates of change, or how quickly quantities are changing. The most convenient way of seeing the changes is to make a graph of them.

For example, the movement of a car at varying speeds can be followed on a graph, with distance up the vertical 'y' axis and time along the horizontal 'x' axis. The car crosses the 'crossroads' at the origin (x = 0, y = 0) and travels at a steady 30 miles an hour. Successive positions of the car (its distance from the origin and correspond-

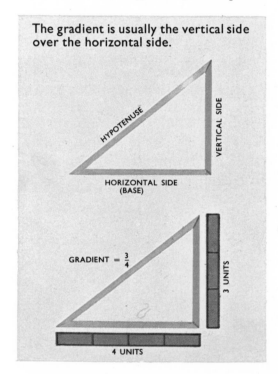

The gradient is usually the vertical side over the horizontal side.

HYPOTENUSE

VERTICAL SIDE

HORIZONTAL SIDE (BASE)

GRADIENT = $\frac{3}{4}$

3 UNITS

4 UNITS

The road gradient is one-in-five. The 'one' is the vertical side of a right-angled triangle, and the 'five' is the sloping side, or hypotenuse.

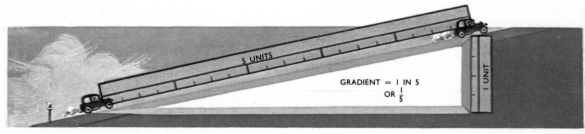

5 UNITS

GRADIENT = 1 IN 5 OR $\frac{1}{5}$

1 UNIT

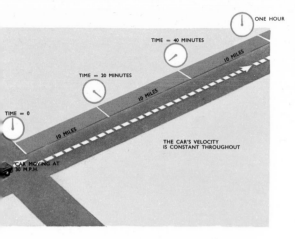

The car crosses the cross-roads at 30 miles per hour. It is timed at various distances from the cross-roads.

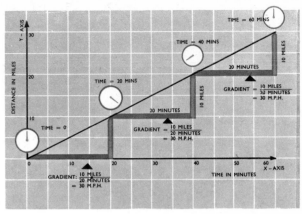

A graph of distance against time. The gradient is a straight line because it represents the velocity which is constant.

ing time) are plotted on the graph, and provided the car keeps going at a steady 30 miles an hour, the graph is a straight line. The gradient of the line is not calculated in the same way as the gradient of the hill.

The gradient is a vertical step divided by its corresponding horizontal step. It can easily be measured by drawing in a right angled triangle with the sloping graph as the hypotenuse. When the horizontal step is one hour, the vertical step is 30 miles.

The gradient is therefore $\frac{30\ miles}{1\ hour}$

which is another way of writing 30 miles per hour, the velocity (or speed) of the car. The gradient of a graph of distance against time is the velocity.

However, it is most unlikely that the car will go for an hour without accelerating or slowing down. If the velocity is constant, the slope of the graph is a constant; the graph is a straight line. But as soon as the car changes its velocity, the slope changes, and the graph becomes curved. This is to be expected, for when the velocity is not constant, the slope is not constant. Nevertheless, the velocity is still given by the gradient of the graph.

The slope of the curve at each instant is equal to the velocity at that same instant.

Although the line may form a smooth curve, it is approximately a succession of short straight lines joined to one another. Each has a slightly different gradient, but, since each little bit is a straight line, its gradient can be calculated in the same way as the gradient of the graph of the car moving at constant speed.

In practice, the best way of finding the gradient from the graph is to move a ruler along the curve until it just touches it. In this position the ruler has the same gradient as the short straight line approximating to the curve. It is the hypotenuse of a triangle. The horizontal and vertical sides of the triangle are drawn in, measured and divided to calculate the gradient.

The gradient of a distance/time graph gives the velocity. Another expression for velocity is 'rate of change of distance with time'. In a similar way, the gradient of a graph showing how the velocity alters with time (i.e. a graph of velocity against time) gives the rate of change of velocity with time – in other words the acceleration.

The gradient after two seconds is 22 feet per second (15 m.p.h.) and after four seconds it is 44 feet per second (30 m.p.h.). It increases because the car is accelerating.

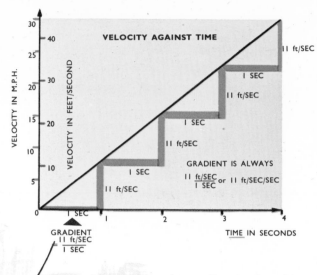

VELOCITY AGAINST TIME

VELOCITY IN M.P.H.

VELOCITY IN FEET/SECOND

11 ft/SEC

1 SEC

11 ft/SEC

1 SEC

11 ft/SEC

1 SEC

11 ft/SEC

1 SEC

11 ft/SEC

GRADIENT IS ALWAYS

$\frac{11 \ ft/SEC}{1 \ SEC}$ or 11 ft/SEC/SEC

TIME IN SECONDS

GRADIENT $\frac{11 \ ft/SEC}{1 \ SEC}$

All curves approximate to a succession of tiny straight lines. The triangles drawn with the straight lines as their hypotenuse give the gradient at each point of a curve.

Velocity (found from the gradients) plotted against time. Now the gradient is the acceleration, *and is constant.*

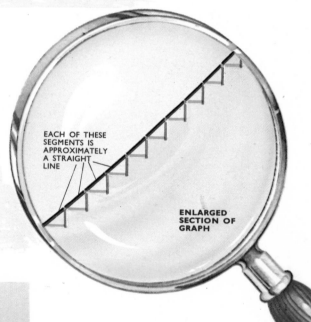

EACH OF THESE SEGMENTS IS APPROXIMATELY A STRAIGHT LINE

ENLARGED SECTION OF GRAPH

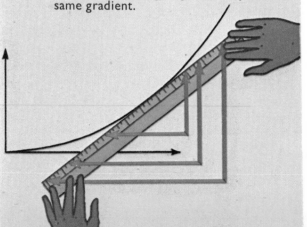

Finding the gradient by moving a ruler along the curve until it just touches it. All these triangles give exactly the same gradient.

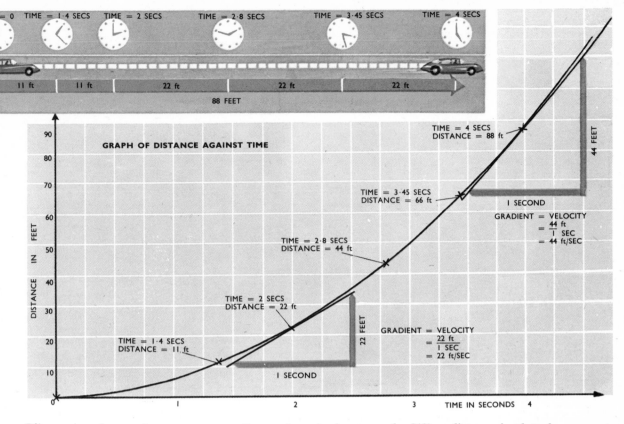

TIME = 0   TIME = 1·4 SECS   TIME = 2 SECS   TIME = 2·8 SECS   TIME = 3·45 SECS   TIME = 4 SECS

11 ft   11 ft   22 ft   22 ft   22 ft

88 FEET

GRAPH OF DISTANCE AGAINST TIME

DISTANCE IN FEET

90
80
70
60
50
40
30
20
10

TIME = 4 SECS
DISTANCE = 88 ft

44 FEET

TIME = 3·45 SECS
DISTANCE = 66 ft

I SECOND

GRADIENT = VELOCITY
= $\frac{44 \text{ ft}}{1 \text{ SEC}}$
= 44 ft/SEC

TIME = 2·8 SECS
DISTANCE = 44 ft

22 FEET

GRADIENT = VELOCITY
= $\frac{22 \text{ ft}}{1 \text{ SEC}}$
= 22 ft/SEC

TIME = 2 SECS
DISTANCE = 22 ft

TIME = 1·4 SECS
DISTANCE = 11 ft

I SECOND

0   1   2   3   TIME IN SECONDS   4

The car accelerates from rest to 30 miles an hour in four seconds. When distance is plotted against time, the graph is not a straight line. The gradient at each point is the velocity at that instant.

CHAPTER TWENTY-FIVE

Graphs and Equations

THE graph drawn from experimental results may turn out to be a smooth curve, or even a straight line. From the shape of the graph, the steepness of its slope and the places where it crosses the 'x' and 'y' axes, it is possible to analyse the results of the experiment, and perhaps deduce the law holding for it.

A graph shows how two quantities vary at the same time. Straight lines which go through the origin show that one of them is proportional to the other. Steps of equal size in the 'x' direction correspond to steps of equal size in the 'y' direction. Another way of saying that they are proportional is that the *ratio* of the set of 'y' values to the set of 'x' values (corresponding members of sets) is constant throughout.

On a graph, the point where the two axes cross is at $x = 0$, $y = 0$. If the graph is a straight line, and it goes through the origin, then 'x' and 'y' are related by a very simple equation $y = mx$.

The sets of values are proportional.

89

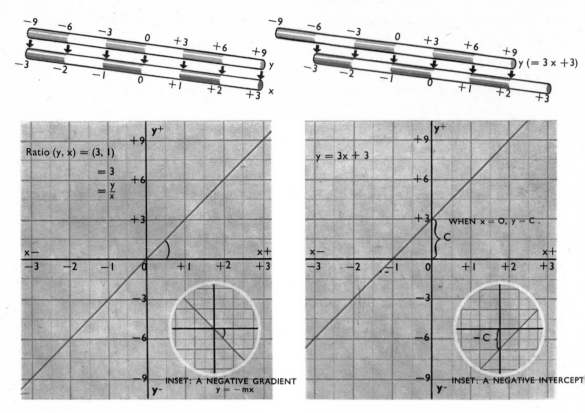

Two parallel number lines can show when two sets of numbers are proportional to each other. The conventional graph consists of two number lines, an 'x' line and a 'y' line, at right angles.

The 'y' line is slid backwards. Now o on the 'x' line is alongside 3 on the 'x' line. y = 3x + 3 for each pair of corresponding points.

The ratio is constant. $y:x$ is the same for all corresponding values of y and x. This ratio value, a number which remains constant throughout the sets, is called m. $y:x = y \div x = m$. To get to $y = mx$, both sides are multiplied by x.

Often a straight line does not score a direct hit on the origin. It misses it and crosses both the y- and the x-axes.

Even then it is possible to deduce the equation of the line. Where the line crosses the vertical y-axis is important. The y-axis marks all points where $x = 0$. When $x = 0$, y has some value. y must be something since it was decided that the line would not go straight through $x = 0, y = 0$. This value is called the *intercept* and is given the symbol c. It stands for a number.

The equation for the line has therefore an additional bit in it. It becomes $y = mx + c$. When $x = 0$, $mx = 0$ and $y = c$. This does happen on the graph.

Curved lines present more problems. It is difficult to get some definite equation out of them. However, curved lines can be used in the opposite direction, i.e. going from an equation to a graph, to solve the equation.

An equation which contains x^1, x^2,

90

x^3, and so on, can be easily drawn on a graph. It is probably much more difficult to solve by other algebraic methods.

For example, $x^2 - x - 2 = 0$. What is x? Instead of solving the equation by algebraic means, $x^2 - x - 2$ is made equal to 'y', the quantity up the vertical axis of the graph. So $y = x^2 - x - 2$. Then x can be given any reasonable values we wish. Enough values are taken for a smooth curve to be drawn. The curve crosses the x-axis in two places. These are the solutions of the equation.

$y = x^2 - x - 2$						
x	-2	-1	0	$+1$	$+2$	$+3$
x^2	$+4$	$+1$	0	$+1$	$+4$	$+9$
$-x$	$+2$	$+1$	0	-1	-2	-3
-2	-2	-2	-2	-2	-2	-2
y	4	0	-2	-2	0	4

Graphs and Proportion

The sets of numbers

$$-9 \quad -6 \quad -3 \quad 0 \quad +3 \quad +6 \quad +9$$
$$-3 \quad -2 \quad -1 \quad 0 \quad +1 \quad +2 \quad +3$$

are proportional and lead to a straight line graph.

The sets of numbers

$$+9 \quad +4 \quad +1 \quad 0 \quad +1 \quad +4 \quad +9$$
$$-3 \quad -2 \quad -1 \quad 0 \quad +1 \quad +2 \quad +3$$

are not proportional and lead to a curved graph instead of a straight line graph. Numbers in the upper set are all the squares (i.e. the number multiplied by itself) of the numbers in the lower set.

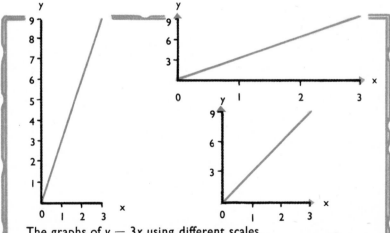

The graphs of $y = 3x$ using different scales.
Altering the scale of either the 'x' or the 'y' number line has no effect on the ratio, m, of the proportional sets. Graph scales are chosen so that the graph fits onto the page.

Why should the solution be given by the points where the curve crosses the x-axis? The reason is that for all points along the x-axis, $y = 0$.

Our graph shows $y = x^2 - x - 2$. But we are especially interested in $0 = x^2 - x - 2$, i.e. the values of x when $y = 0$.

If a curve of this form cuts a line at all, it cuts it in two places (except when it just touches the curve – this is a special case). It could happen that the curve stays clear away from the x-axis. This is an indication that there is no real solution to the equation.

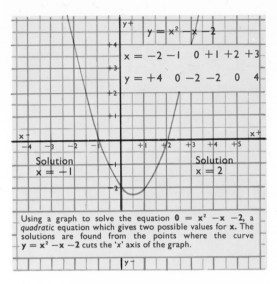

$y = x^2 - x - 2$						
$x =$	-2	-1	0	$+1$	$+2$	$+3$
$y =$	$+4$	0	-2	-2	0	4

Solution $x = -1$ Solution $x = 2$

Using a graph to solve the equation $0 = x^2 - x - 2$, a *quadratic* equation which gives two possible values for **x**. The solutions are found from the points where the curve $y = x^2 - x - 2$ cuts the 'x' axis of the graph.

SOLUTIONS OF GRAPHS WITH THE LINE $y = 0$

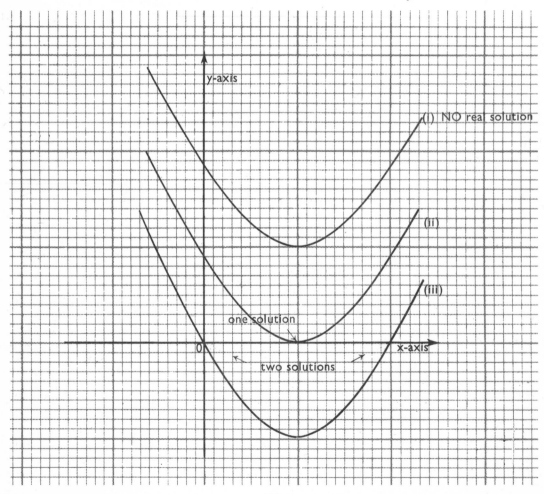

y-axis

(I) NO real solution

(ii)

(iii)

one solution

0   x-axis

two solutions

92

CHAPTER TWENTY-SIX

The Area Under a Graph

THE two important things which can be calculated from a graph are its slope, or gradient, and the area underneath it. The gradient shows how the two quantities involved on the graph are varying; in other words it is the *rate of change*. The slope of a graph of distance against time is the rate of change of distance with time – i.e. the *velocity*. The slope of a graph of velocity against time gives the rate of change of velocity with time – i.e. the *acceleration*. The slope of a graph of acceleration against time gives the

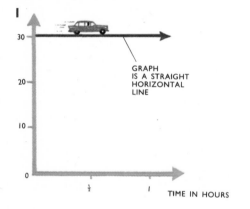

The car travels at a steady 30 miles per hour. Its velocity is constant.

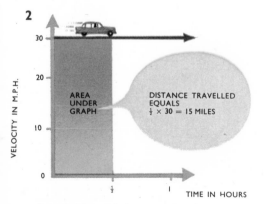

After one hour. Distance travelled equals velocity (30 m.p.h.) multiplied by time (one hour), the area of the rectangle.

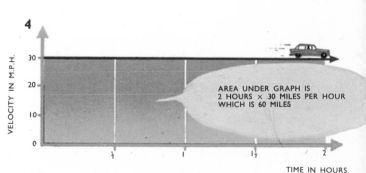

The position of the car after ½ hour. As the car travels, the area under the line increases.

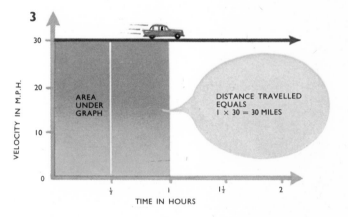

The area under a graph of velocity against time always gives the distance travelled, even when the line is sloping or curved. The branch of mathematics which deals with finding areas under graphs is called integral calculus.

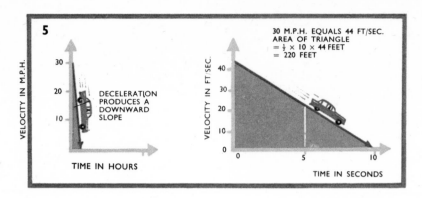

The car decelerates steadily in ten seconds, coming to a halt. This time is so short that it is better to change the scales of the graph (as in the diagram on the right). The area under the graph is a triangle.

rate of change of acceleration with time, and so on. The sequence is distance – velocity – acceleration – rate of change of acceleration. Areas also have a sequence, but it goes in the opposite direction. The area under a graph of *rate of change of acceleration* against *time* gives the *acceleration*. The area under a graph of *acceleration* against *time* gives the *velocity*. The sequence is working backwards, for the area under the *velocity* against *time* graph gives the *distance* travelled.

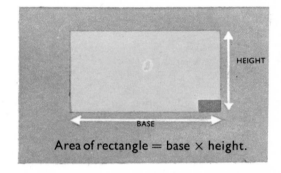

Area of rectangle = base × height.

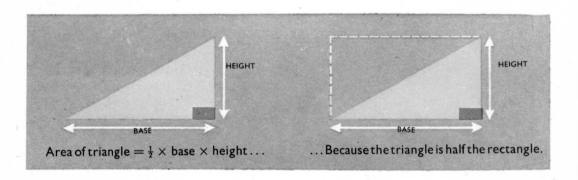

Area of triangle = ½ × base × height... ...Because the triangle is half the rectangle.

Trigonometry

CHAPTER TWENTY-SEVEN

Ratio and Proportion

THE set of numbers 12, 24, 36, 48 has an important property in common with the set 2, 4, 6, 8. The numbers in the first set are all 6 times bigger than the corresponding numbers in the second set. A comparison and read as 12 is to 2; 24 is to 4, etc. In each case the ratio simplifies out to $\frac{6}{1}$ or 6 : 1. If one set of numbers were plotted against the other set of numbers on rectangular axes, the

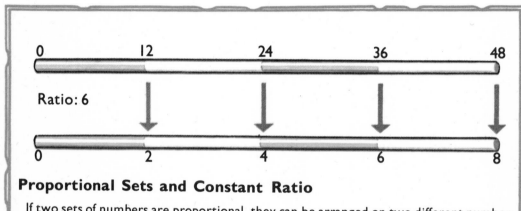

Proportional Sets and Constant Ratio

If two sets of numbers are proportional, they can be arranged on two different number lines so that all the members of one set correspond to members of the other set. The ratio (number in first set) : (number in second set) is constant.

of the numbers in pairs is called a RATIO. A ratio is defined as the relationship between two quantities measured in the same units and is therefore a relationship between *numbers* only, the units cancelling out.

In the case under discussion the relationship between the first set of numbers 12, 24, 36, 48 and the second set of numbers 2, 4, 6, 8 is written in the ratio form either as $\frac{12}{2}, \frac{24}{4}, \frac{36}{6}, \frac{48}{8}$, or as 12 : 2; 24 : 4; 36 : 6; 48 : 8

join of the points would give a straight line. An equality of ratios introduces another mathematical concept called PROPORTION.

If a man walks at a steady rate of 4 m.p.h. the distance he covers will increase in a definite way. In one hour he covers 4 miles, in two hours 8 miles and so on.

Time in hours: 1   2   3   4
Distance in miles: 4   8   12   16
The ratios of times and the ratios

of corresponding distances are always the same.

$$\frac{1 \text{ hr}}{2 \text{ hr}} = \frac{4 \text{ miles}}{8 \text{ miles}} = \frac{1}{2}$$

$$\frac{2 \text{ hr}}{4 \text{ hr}} = \frac{8 \text{ miles}}{16 \text{ miles}} = \frac{1}{2}$$

(with headings *Time   Distance* above)

In this problem we notice that when the *time increases*, the *distance* also *increases*. Such a proportional is called a *direct* proportion.

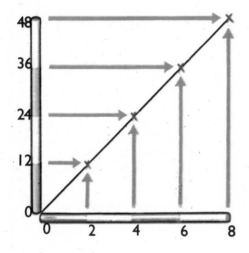

The usual kind of graph paper is like two number lines at right angles to each other. Proportional sets give a straight line.

The fraction $\dfrac{\text{Time}}{\text{Distance}}$ is a constant quantity. Put in another way, time varies directly as the distance. In another kind of problem we might have a different kind of proportional relationship. For example: If 12 men mow a field in 8 days, then 24 men working at the same rate will obviously take a shorter time of 4 days to mow the same field. This means that if the number of men on the job is doubled the time is cut down to half, and the relationship is written

Men   Days

$$\frac{12}{24} \qquad \frac{4}{8}$$

the 12 and 8 being the connecting figures in the given statement.

Thus we find that when the number of *men increases*, the number of *days decreases* and we have what is mathematically known as an *inverse* or *indirect* proportion.

The fraction $\dfrac{\text{men}}{\frac{1}{\text{days}}}$ is a constant quantity, or, men × days gives the constant value. In the first problem, if we plotted time against distance a straight line would result. In the second problem we would have to plot men against $\dfrac{1}{\text{days}}$ to get a straight line.

Generally a proportion between four numbers is written as $\dfrac{a}{b} = \dfrac{c}{d}$. This is a simple equation involving *four* quantities and d is called the *fourth* proportional and can be found if a, b and c are known quantities. If the proportion is written as $\dfrac{a}{b} = \dfrac{b}{c}$ involving *three* quantities, then c is called the *third* proportional and can be found if a and b are known. In the same relationship b is called the *mean* proportional; $\dfrac{a}{b} = \dfrac{b}{c}$ transforms by cross-multiplication to $b^2 = ac$ giving $b = \sqrt{ac}$ and b can be found if a and c are known.

97

Geometrical Representation and Proportion

To obtain the FOURTH proportional to three given lengths.

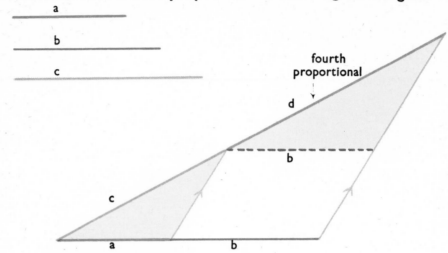

The shaded triangles are similar and their corresponding sides are proportional giving $\frac{a}{b}=\frac{c}{d}$ and therefore d is the *fourth* proportional

To obtain the THIRD proportional to two given lengths.

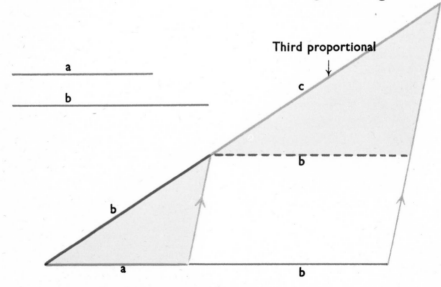

The shaded triangles are similar and again we have $\frac{a}{b}=\frac{b}{c}$ and therefore c is the THIRD proportional

To obtain the **MEAN** proportional to two given lengths.

_____ a

_____ c

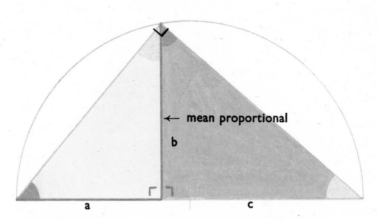

The shaded triangles are equiangular and similar and have
their corresponding sides proportional giving $\frac{a}{b} = \frac{b}{c}$ and b is therefore the
MEAN proportional

The construction of the mean proportional is the same as constructing the side of a square
which has the same area as the rectangle whose sides are the lengths 'a' and 'c'.
To draw a square equal in area to a given rectangle:

_____ a

_____ c

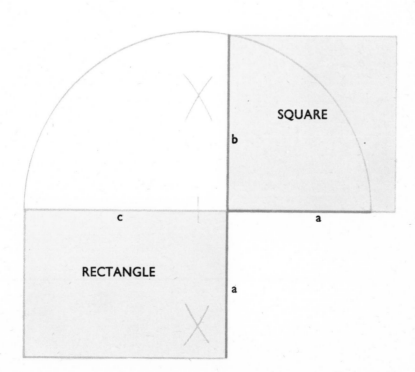

SQUARE

b

c

a

RECTANGLE

a

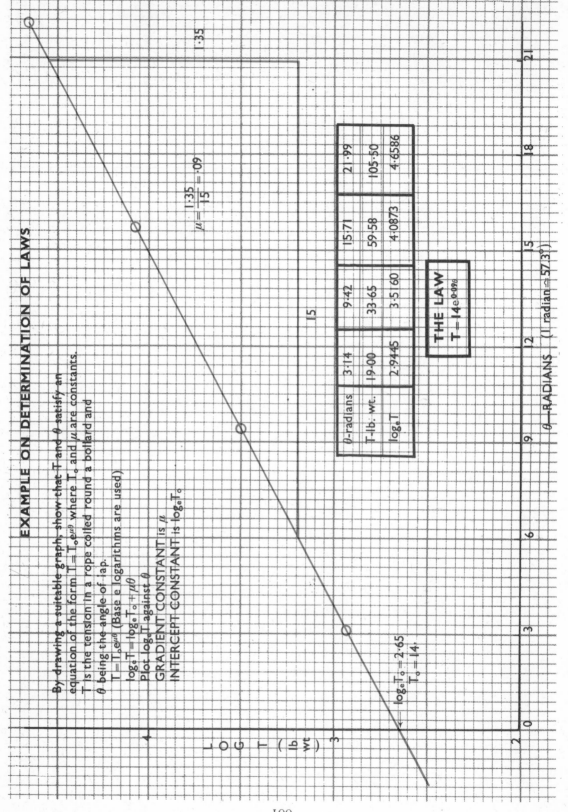

EXAMPLE ON DETERMINATION OF LAWS

By drawing a suitable graph, show that T and θ satisfy an equation of the form $T = T_0 e^{\mu\theta}$ where T_0 and μ are constants. T is the tension in a rope coiled round a bollard and θ being the angle of lap.

$T = T_0 e^{\mu\theta}$ (Base e logarithms are used)

$\log_e T = \log_e T_0 + \mu\theta$

Plot $\log_e T$ against θ

GRADIENT CONSTANT is μ

INTERCEPT CONSTANT is $\log_e T_0$

$\mu = \dfrac{1.35}{15} = .09$

θ-radians	3.14	9.42	15.71	21.99
T-lb. wt.	19.00	33.65	59.58	105.50
$\log_e T$	2.9445	3.5160	4.0873	4.6586

THE LAW $T = 14 e^{0.09\theta}$

$\log_e T_0 = 2.65$, $T_0 = 14$.

LOG T (lb wt)

θ—RADIANS (1 radian $\simeq$ 57.3°)

Determination of Laws

Experimental engineering provides many instances in which a law relating two variables is determined from data obtained by practical experiment. If the general form of the law is known it can be amended into a linear form. By graphical representation the constants can be determined and the law found.

Some common forms of equations are tabulated below.

LAW	LINEAR FORM		PLOT Y against X	CONSTANTS	
				Gradient	Intercept
(i) $y = a + \dfrac{b}{x}$	$y = b\left(\dfrac{1}{x}\right) + a$	$Y = bX + a$	$X \equiv \dfrac{1}{x}$	b	a
(ii) $y = a + \dfrac{b}{x^2}$	$y = b\left(\dfrac{1}{x^2}\right) + a$	$Y = bX + a$	$X \equiv \dfrac{1}{x^2}$	b	a
(iii) $y = \dfrac{a}{x} + bx$	$\dfrac{y}{x} = \dfrac{a}{x^2} + b$	$Y = aX + b$	$Y \equiv \dfrac{y}{x}$	a	b
			$X \equiv \dfrac{1}{x^2}$		
(iv) $y = ax^n$	$\log y = \log a + n \log x$	$Y = nX + \log a$	$Y \equiv \log y$ $X \equiv \log x$	n	$\log a$
(v) $y = bc^x$	$\log y = \log b + (\log c)x$	$Y = \log c(X) + \log b$	$Y \equiv \log y$ $X \equiv x$	$\log c$	$\log b$

Trigonometric Ratios

THE solution of a triangle from information insufficient to solve it completely by elementary arithmetic or algebraic methods is solved by the method of *trigonometrical* calculations. Sometimes this branch of mathematics is called triangulation. It also is a method of measuring an angle without using a protractor, the practical, direct-reading instrument used for the purpose. The right-angled triangle is the simplest type of triangle to deal with. The practical problem is sometimes mapped into a right-angled triangle for solution. In any right-angled triangle the ratio of the sides provides a method for finding the angles. Since the triangle has three sides, they can be arranged in three direct ratio forms. The names given to the ratios are associated with the names given to the sides of the triangle.

When the ratios are worked out and the value referred to the appropriate set of trigonometrical tables, the

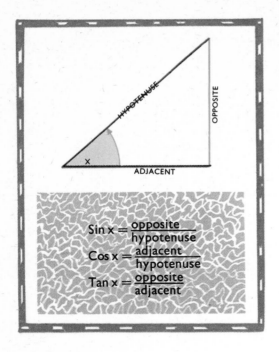

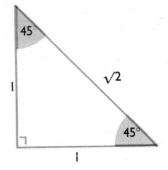

The ratios of angles 45°, 30° and 60° can be worked out without reference to any tables because of the particular type of right-angled triangle in which they can be found.

The Right-angled Isosceles Triangle

$$\sin 45° = \frac{1}{\sqrt{2}} = \frac{\sqrt{2}}{2} = \frac{1\cdot4140}{2}$$
$$= 0\cdot7070$$
$$\cos 45° = \frac{1}{\sqrt{2}} = 0\cdot7070$$
$$\tan 45° = \frac{1}{1} = 1\cdot0000$$

angle is discovered. It is a well-known mathematical fact that if an angle in any set of right-angled triangles remains constant the ratio of corresponding sides also remains constant and is therefore independent of the lengths of the sides.

An instrument like this is called a theodolite *and is used by surveyors to measure angles.*

These values for the ratios of the angle 45° are the same whatever the size of the triangle because of the nature of the right-angled triangle – isosceles and right-angled – in which the angle 45° always occurs.

The Equilateral Triangle

The values of the ratios of the angles of 30° and 60° are the same whatever the size of the triangle because of the nature of the right-angled triangle (half of an equilateral triangle) in which they occur.

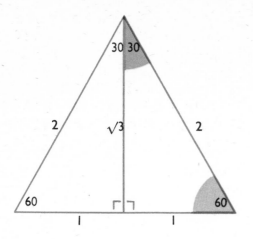

0° and becomes equal to the length of the ruler when the angle is 90°. Since the sine of an angle is the ratio of the opposite side to the hypotenuse, this ratio is zero when the angle is 0°, and 1 when the angle is 90°. So we have $\sin 0° = 0$ and $\sin 90° = 1$. Therefore as the *angle* increases from 0° to 90° the *value* of the sine *ratio* of an angle *increases* from 0 to 1. The value of the ratio can never be greater than 1. This is also true because the ratio expressed as a fraction has the hypotenuse, which is the longest side of the triangle, in the denominator.

$$\sin 30° = \frac{1}{2} = 0{\cdot}5000$$

$$\cos 30° = \frac{\sqrt{3}}{2} = \frac{1{\cdot}7320}{2} = 0{\cdot}8660$$

$$\tan 30° = \frac{1}{\sqrt{3}} = \frac{\sqrt{3}}{3} = \frac{1{\cdot}7320}{3}$$
$$= 0{\cdot}5773$$

$$\sin 60° = \frac{\sqrt{3}}{2} = \frac{1{\cdot}7320}{2} = 0{\cdot}8660$$

$$\cos 60° = \frac{1}{2} = 0{\cdot}5000$$

$$\tan 60° = \frac{\sqrt{3}}{1} = 1{\cdot}7320$$

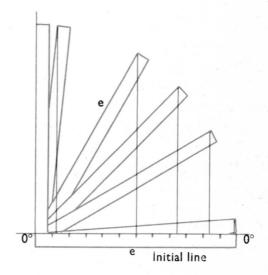

initial line

The Nature of the Sine Ratio

If a ruler pivoted at 0 is rotated from an initial line slowly, its edge traces out gradually increasing angles from 0° to 90°. The ruler itself forms the hypotenuse of a right-angled triangle at any stage of its rotation, if a perpendicular is dropped on to the initial line from its end. The side in the right-angled triangle opposite to the angle at the centre of rotation increases as the angle increases from 0° to 90°. It vanishes when the angle is

The Nature of the Cosine Ratio

We notice from the ruler diagram that when the opposite side changes from nothing to the length of the ruler, the adjacent side changes in the reverse way. This gives the $\cos 0° = 1$ and $\cos 90° = 0$. Therefore as the *angle* increases from 0° to 90° the *value* of the cosine *ratio* of an angle *decreases* from 1 to 0. Again the cosine ratio can never be greater than 1 for the same reasons.

Reading the Trigonometrical Tables

Natural Sines

	0′	6′	12′	18′	24′	30′	36′	42′	48′	54′	1′	2′	3′	4′	5′
0°	0·0000	0017	0035	0052	0070	0087	0105	0122	0140	0157	3	6	9	12	15
1	0·0175	0192	0209	0227	0244	0262	0279	0297	0314	0332	3	6	9	12	15
2	0·0349	0366	0384	0401	0419	0436	0454	0471	0488	0506	3	6	9	12	15
3	0·0523	0541	0558	0576	0593	0610	0628	0645	0663	0680	3	6	9	12	15
4	0·0698	0715	0732	0750	0767	0785	0802	0819	0837	0854	3	6	9	12	14
5	0·0872	0889	0906	0924	0941	0958	0976	0993	1011	1028	3	6	9	12	14
6	0·1045	1063	1080	1097	1115	1132	1149	1167	1184	1201	3	6	9	12	14
7	0·1219	1236	1253	1271	1288	1305	1323	1340	1357	1374	3	6	9	12	14
8	0·1392	1409	1426	1444	1461	1478	1495	1513	1530	1547	3	6	9	12	14
9	0·1564	1582	1599	1616	1633	1650	1668	1685	1702	1719	3	6	9	11	14
10	0·1736	1754	1771	1788	1805	1822	1840	1857	1874	1891	3	6	9	11	14
11	0·1908	1925	1942	1959	1977	1994	2011	2028	2045	2062	3	6	9	11	14

An angle is very rarely a whole number of degrees and so the tables are designed to read fractions of a degree in fact to the nearest minute. The column headings are spaced out at 6 minute intervals 0, 6, 12, 18, etc., and the missing five minutes between these intervals are accounted for in the adjacent columns numbered 1, 2, 3, 4, 5.

sin 9° 45′

sin 9° 42′ = 0·1685

sin 9° 45′ — sin 9° 42′ = 0·0009 for diff. o[f]

add   sin 9° 45′ = 0·1694

Natural Cosines

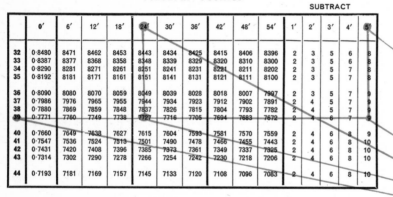

SUBTRACT

	0′	6′	12′	18′	24′	30′	36′	42′	48′	54′	1′	2′	3′	4′	5′
32	0·8480	8471	8462	8453	8443	8434	8425	8415	8406	8396	2	3	5	6	8
33	0·8387	8377	8368	8358	8348	8339	8329	8320	8310	8300	2	3	5	6	8
34	0·8290	8281	8271	8261	8251	8241	8231	8221	8211	8202	2	3	5	7	8
35	0·8192	8181	8171	8161	8151	8141	8131	8121	8111	8100	2	3	5	7	8
36	0·8090	8080	8070	8059	8049	8039	8028	8018	8007	7997	2	3	5	7	9
37	0·7986	7976	7965	7955	7944	7934	7923	7912	7902	7891	2	4	5	7	9
38	0·7880	7869	7859	7848	7837	7826	7815	7804	7793	7782	2	4	5	7	9
39	0·7771	7760	7749	7738	7727	7716	7705	7694	7683	7672	2	4	6	7	9
40	0·7660	7649	7638	7627	7615	7604	7593	7581	7570	7559	2	4	6	8	9
41	0·7547	7536	7524	7513	7501	7490	7478	7466	7455	7443	2	4	6	8	10
42	0·7431	7420	7408	7396	7385	7373	7361	7349	7337	7325	2	4	6	8	10
43	0·7314	7302	7290	7278	7266	7254	7242	7230	7218	7206	2	4	6	8	10
44	0·7193	7181	7169	7157	7145	7133	7120	7108	7096	7083	2	4	6	8	10

cos 39° 29′

cos 39° 24′ = 0·7727

cos 39° 24′ — cos 39° 29′ = 0·0009 for diff. o[f]

subtract   cos 39° 29′ = 0·7768

Natural Tangents

	0′	6′	12′	18′	24′	30′	36′	42′	48′	54′	1′	2′	3′	4′	5′
48°	1·1106	1145	1184	1224	1263	1303	1343	1383	1423	1463	7	13	20	26	33
49	1·1504	1544	1585	1626	1667	1708	1750	1792	1833	1875	7	14	21	28	34
50	1·1918	1960	2002	2045	2088	2131	2174	2218	2261	2305	7	14	22	29	36
51	1·2349	2393	2437	2482	2527	2572	2617	2662	2708	2753	8	15	23	30	38
52	1·2799	2846	2892	2938	2985	3032	3079	3127	3175	3222	8	16	24	31	39
53	1·3270	3319	3367	3416	3465	3514	3564	3613	3663	3713	8	16	25	33	41
54	1·3764	3814	3865	3916	3968	4019	4071	4124	4176	4229	9	17	26	34	43
55	1·4281	4335	4388	4442	4496	4550	4605	4659	4715	4770	9	18	27	36	45

tan 53° 8′

tan 53° 6′ = 1·3319

tan 53° 8′ — tan 53° 6′ = 0·0016 for diff. o[f]

add   tan 53° 8′ = 1·3335

The Nature of the Tangent Ratio

When the angle is zero, that is when the ruler is on the initial line, the *opposite* side vanishes and the *adjacent* side is the same length as the ruler. Therefore $\tan 0° = \frac{0}{1} = 0$. When the angle is 90°, that is when the ruler is perpendicular to the initial line, the adjacent side vanishes and the opposite side is the length of the ruler. The tangent ratio of 90° is therefore $\frac{\text{ruler length}}{0}$ and this result is very big indeed—in fact it is infinity and in mathematics is written ∞. When the angle is 45°, the opposite side is equal to the adjacent side and $\tan 45° = 1$, which is the value we have already found for $\tan 45°$.

Summary of These Results

Ratio ╲ Angle	0°	30°	45°	60°	90°
sin	0	$\frac{1}{2}$	$\frac{1}{\sqrt{2}}$	$\frac{\sqrt{3}}{2}$	1
cos	1	$\frac{\sqrt{3}}{2}$	$\frac{1}{\sqrt{2}}$	$\frac{1}{2}$	0
tan	0	$\frac{1}{\sqrt{3}}$	1	$\sqrt{3}$	∞

From this table of results it can be seen that $\sin 30° = \cos 60°$, $\sin 60° = \cos 30°$ and $\sin 45° = \cos 45°$.

Since the pairs of angles in each set add up to 90°, the sine and cosine ratios are said to be complementary in character. Generally
$$\sin \theta° = \cos (90 - \theta) \text{ or}$$
$$\cos \theta° = \sin (90 - \theta).$$

Using the Trigonometrical Ratios to Solve Right-angled Triangles

The ratios represent three inter-dependent quantities, two sides and one angle in a right-angled triangle. If the two sides are known then the angle can be found and if one side and the angle are known then the other side can be found.

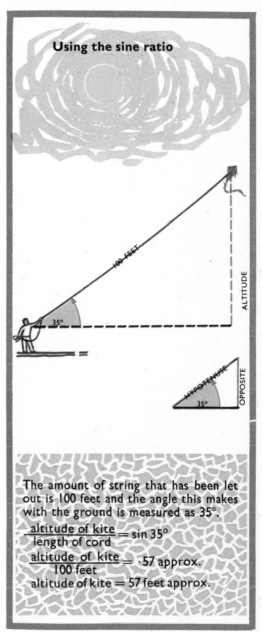

Using the sine ratio

The amount of string that has been let out is 100 feet and the angle this makes with the ground is measured as 35°.

$$\frac{\text{altitude of kite}}{\text{length of cord}} = \sin 35°$$

$$\frac{\text{altitude of kite}}{100 \text{ feet}} = \cdot 57 \text{ approx.}$$

altitude of kite = 57 feet approx.

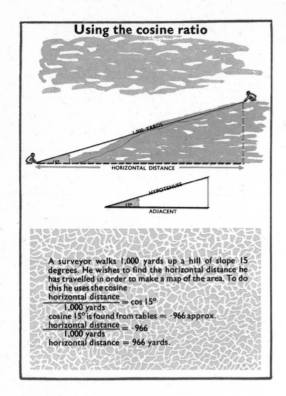

Using the cosine ratio

1,000 YARDS

15°

HORIZONTAL DISTANCE

HYPOTENUSE

15°

ADJACENT

A surveyor walks 1,000 yards up a hill of slope 15 degrees. He wishes to find the horizontal distance he has travelled in order to make a map of the area. To do this he uses the cosine

$$\frac{\text{horizontal distance}}{1,000 \text{ yards}} = \cos 15°$$

cosine 15° is found from tables = ·966 approx.

$$\frac{\text{horizontal distance}}{1,000 \text{ yards}} = ·966$$

horizontal distance = 966 yards.

Using the tangent ratio

OPPOSITE

62°

ADJACENT

62°

100 FEET

$$\frac{\text{height of monument}}{\text{distance of observer from base}} = \tan 62°$$

$$\frac{\text{height of monument}}{100 \text{ feet}} = 1·88 \text{ approx.}$$

height of monument = 188 feet approx.

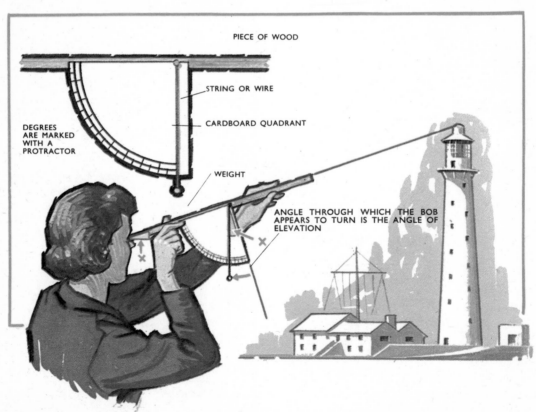

PIECE OF WOOD

STRING OR WIRE

CARDBOARD QUADRANT

DEGREES ARE MARKED WITH A PROTRACTOR

WEIGHT

ANGLE THROUGH WHICH THE BOB APPEARS TO TURN IS THE ANGLE OF ELEVATION

How to make and use a simple sextant to measure angles of elevation and angles of depression.

An *angle of elevation* is the angle made by the directions of the *line of sight* and the *horizontal*

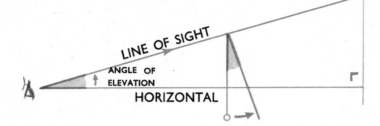

LINE OF SIGHT

ANGLE OF ELEVATION

HORIZONTAL

Angle of DEPRESSION

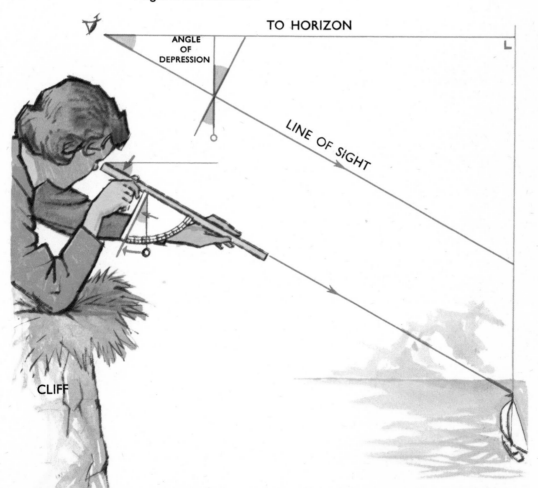

TO HORIZON

ANGLE OF DEPRESSION

LINE OF SIGHT

CLIFF

Angle of depression is the angle made by the directions of the *line of sight* and the *horizon*.
If the positions of the OBSERVER and OBSERVED were interchanged the angle of ELEVATION is equal to the angle of DEPRESSION.

The peaks of the track are maxima and the bottoms of the dips are minima. Maxima and minima are turning points in the slope of the track.

MAXIMA AND MINIMA

Calculus

CHAPTER TWENTY-NINE

Introduction to the Calculus

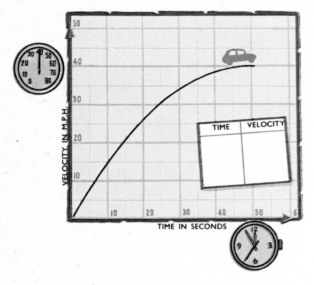

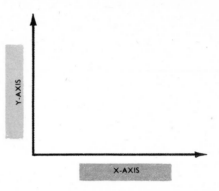

Graphs picture how two quantities vary. Left: Velocity varying with time. Above: Often the quantities are called simply 'x' and 'y'.

CALCULUS comes from a word meaning simply 'to calculate', but in mathematics it includes only a specialized type of calculation. Calculus deals with the way things change in relation to one another. Sir Isaac

Calculus deals with infinitely small changes. A curve is broken up into a great many tiny straight lines. Small changes in x and y taking place over one straight line are called δx and δy. When these become infinitely small, they are called dx and dy. dy divided by dx is the gradient of the curve.

Newton, one of the originators of calculus, had a better name for it – the *method of fluxions*.

The best way of showing how things change is to represent them on a graph. A graph with two axes, an 'x' axis and a 'y' axis pictures how one quantity (represented by 'y') changes when the other quantity (represented by 'x') changes. The value of y for any

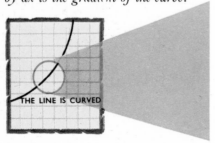

THE LINE IS CURVED

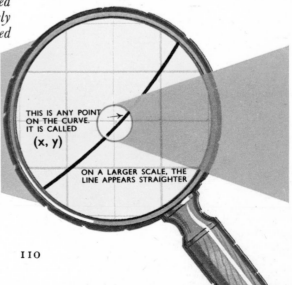

THIS IS ANY POINT ON THE CURVE. IT IS CALLED

(x, y)

ON A LARGER SCALE, THE LINE APPEARS STRAIGHTER

value of x can be found simply by looking at the graph, and this is the most important piece of information that a graph provides.

Another thing that can be found from the graph is the *rate-of-change of y with x*. This is the *slope*, or *gradient* of the graph.

It is easy to find the gradient of a straight line graph. The gradient is the same anywhere along the line. If part of the line is made the sloping side, (or *hypotenuse*) of a right-angled triangle, by drawing in the vertical side and the horizontal side, the gradient is the length of the vertical side divided by the length of the horizontal side.

Straight line graphs are common in science. They occur when the quantity represented by 'x' is directly proportional to the quantity represented by 'y'.

When the graph is a curved line, the gradient varies from point to point along it. But, at any point, it can be found by moving a ruler until it just touches the line at this point. The ruler then lies along the sloping side of the triangle which gives the gradient at this particular point.

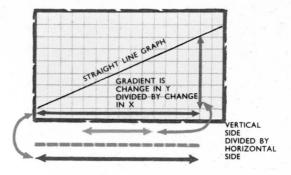

The gradient of a straight line is the same at all points along the line. Any right-angled triangle with the line as its hypotenuse gives the gradient.

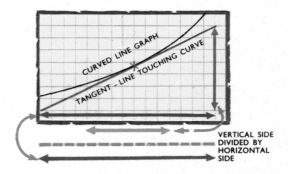

The gradient at any point along a curve can be found from the line touching the curve at this point. The gradient varies from point to point.

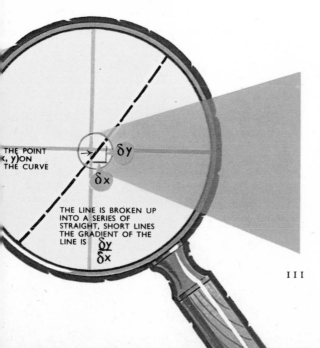

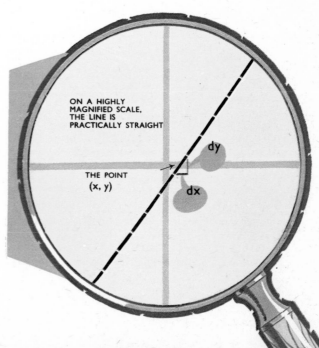

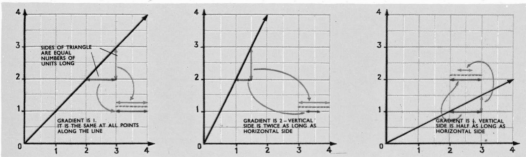

Left: This is the graph of y = x. If x = 1, y = 1, if x = 3, y = 3, and so on. The gradient of this line is 1. Centre: The graph of y = 2x. The gradient is 2. Right: The graph of y = ½x. The gradient is ½. All graphs where y = just a number multiplied by x are straight lines. The gradient of the straight line is the number in front of x.

In calculus, a curved line is imagined to be made up of an infinitely large number of infinitely small straight lines, joined end to end. The gradient at any point then becomes the gradient of the infinitely small straight line at that point. Over the small portion of the graph covered by the straight line, both 'x' and 'y' change by tiny amounts. The symbols used for the small changes are δx and δy (delta-x and delta-y).

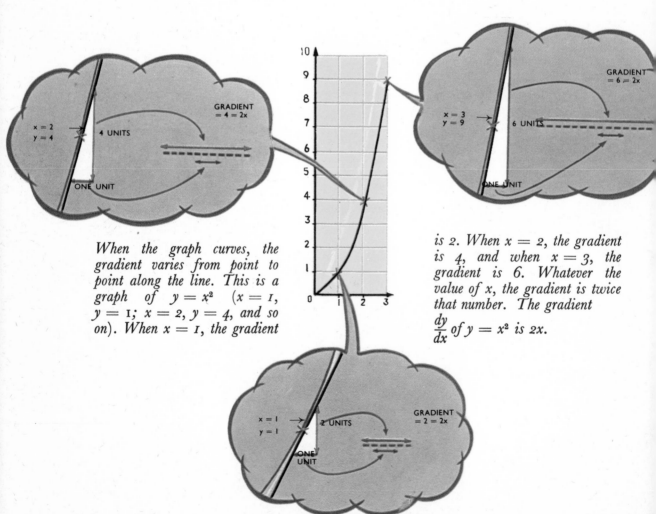

When the graph curves, the gradient varies from point to point along the line. This is a graph of y = x² (x = 1, y = 1; x = 2, y = 4, and so on). When x = 1, the gradient is 2. *When x = 2, the gradient is 4, and when x = 3, the gradient is 6. Whatever the value of x, the gradient is twice that number. The gradient* $\frac{dy}{dx}$ *of y = x² is 2x.*

δx is the horizontal side of a triangle and δy is the vertical side. The gradient of the sloping side is δy divided by δx (the vertical side divided by the horizontal side) i.e. $\frac{\delta y}{\delta x}$. When δx and δy become so small that they are almost equal to nothing, they are called dx and dy. The gradient of the sloping graph is then $\frac{dy}{dx}$ where $\frac{dy}{dx}$ is the *rate-of-change of y with x*, and it is called the *derivative*. The process of finding $\frac{dy}{dx}$ is called *differentiation*.

A graph shows how one quantity changes when another quantity changes. For example, the change in velocity (v) of a car with time (t) can be shown by plotting a graph of v against t. The derivative is then $\frac{dv}{dt}$. This is the rate of change of the car's velocity with time – in other words, its *acceleration*. In practice the derivative is not usually found from the graph itself. $\frac{dy}{dx}$ or $\frac{dv}{dt}$ are nearly always found by applying simple algebraic rules.

CHAPTER THIRTY

Differentiating from First Principles

IF $y = x^2$ is the curve under consideration and (x, y) is any point on it, then any neighbouring point on the curve is given by (x + δx, y + δy). The same condition governs both points, and therefore, if

$$y = x^2$$
so $\quad y + \delta y = (x + \delta x)^2$
$$y + \delta y = x^2 + 2x\delta x + (\delta x)^2$$
From these relationships we get
$$x^2 + \delta y = x^2 + 2x\delta x + (\delta x)^2$$
$$\delta y = 2x\delta x + (\delta x)^2$$
Dividing through by δx
$$\frac{\delta y}{\delta x} = 2x + \delta x$$

Now as δx approaches zero, δy also approaches zero and $\frac{\delta y}{\delta x}$ becomes $\frac{dy}{dx}$.

This means that whereas $\frac{\delta y}{\delta x}$ was the average gradient of the curve between the points (x, y) and (x + δx), (y + δy), $\frac{dy}{dx}$ is the actual gradient of the curve at the point (x, y) itself. The symbol for the gradient at a given point on the curve is therefore $\frac{dy}{dx}$. This is expressed mathematically as follows:

$$\underset{\delta x \to 0}{\mathcal{L}t}\ \frac{\delta y}{\delta x} = \frac{dy}{dx} \quad \text{and}$$

represents the limit as δx tends to 0, and therefore $\quad \frac{\delta y}{\delta x} = 2x + \delta x$

becomes $\quad\quad \frac{dy}{dx} = 2x$

Since x is a quantity which can take any value, $\frac{dy}{dx}$ changes with x which is a way of describing any curve; an alteration in position and therefore in the value of x results in an alteration of slope or gradient. Thus for the curve $y = x^2$, if x has the values 1, 2, 3 and 4, $\frac{dy}{dx}$ has the values 2, 4, 6 and 8.

Step I

Applying Simple Algebra

At all points along the graph –

$$y = 2x^2$$
$$\text{Also } y + \delta y = 2(x + \delta x)^2$$
$$y + \delta y = 2x^2 + 4x \cdot \delta x + 2(\delta x)^2$$

But $y = 2x^2$, always. So both y and $2x^2$ can be cancelled out of the equation. So the remaining part of the equation is

$$\delta y = 4x \cdot \delta x + 2(\delta x)^2.$$

The Multiplied Constant

If instead of $y = x^2$ we take $y = 2x^2$, multiplying x^2 by 2 (a constant) and carrying through with the same mathematical operations and arguments, we get

$$y + \delta y = 2(x + \delta x)^2$$
$$= 2(x^2 + 2x\delta x + \delta x^2)$$
$$2x^2 + \delta y = 2x^2 + 4x\delta x + 2\delta x^2$$
$$\delta y = 4x\delta x + 2\delta x^2$$
$$\frac{\delta y}{\delta x} = 4x + 2\delta x$$
$$\underset{\delta x \to 0}{\mathcal{L}t} \; \frac{\delta y}{\delta x} = \frac{dy}{dx} = 4x \text{ or } 2(2x).$$

Thus we see that the gradient at any

Step 2

Then, after finding out what happens algebraically, it is possible to start on calculus.

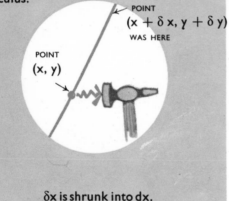

POINT
(x + δ x, y + δ y)
WAS HERE

POINT
(x, y)

δx is shrunk into dx.

The sizes of δx and δy are now shrunk enormously, turning them into dx and dy.

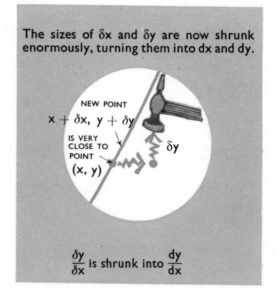

NEW POINT
x + δx, y + δy

IS VERY CLOSE TO POINT
(x, y)

δy

$\dfrac{\delta y}{\delta x}$ is shrunk into $\dfrac{dy}{dx}$

Step 3

δx and δy, although they are very small indeed, are not small enough to be neglected.

But $(\delta x)^2$ is very small indeed –

it can be taken out from the equation.

So $\delta y = 4x \cdot \delta x + 2(\delta x)^2$

Dividing through by δx and letting $\delta x \to 0$

$$\frac{dy}{dx} = 4x$$

GRAPHS SHOWING MULTIPLIED AND
ADDED CONSTANTS WITH GRADIENTS

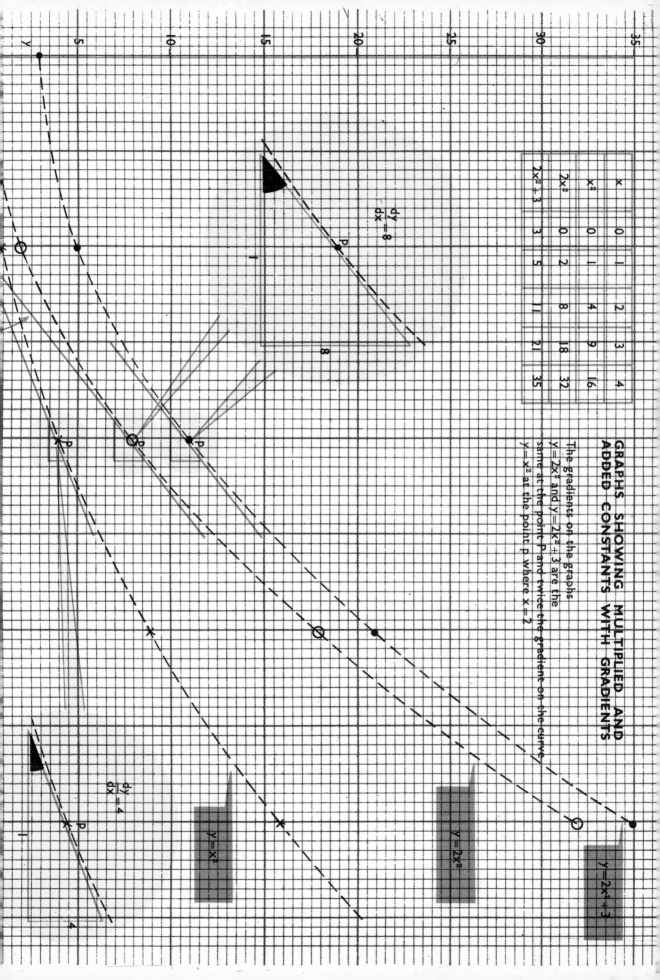

x	0	1	2	3	4
x²	0	1	4	9	16
2x²	0	2	8	18	32
2x²+3	3	5	11	21	35

The gradients on the graphs
$y = 2x^2$ and $y = 2x^2 + 3$ are the
same at the point P and twice the
same as the gradient on the curve
$y = x^2$ at the point P where $x = 2$

$\frac{dy}{dx} = 8$

$\frac{dy}{dx} = 4$

$y = x^2$

$y = 2x^2$

$y = 2x^2 + 3$

point on this curve is *twice* the value of the gradient on the first curve $y = x^2$. Thus the effect of the multiplied constant is to multiply the gradient by the constant quantity.

The Added Constant

If instead of $y = 2x^2$ we take the curve $y = 2x^2 + 3$, adding a constant quantity 3 to $2x^2$, and continue as before

$$y = 2x^2 + 3$$
$$y + \delta y = 2(x + \delta x)^2 + 3$$
$$y + \delta y = 2(x^2 + 2x\delta x + \delta x^2) + 3$$
$$2x^2 + 3 + \delta y = 2x^2 + 4x\delta x + 2\delta x^2 + 3$$
$$\delta y = 4x\delta x + \delta 2x^2$$
$$\frac{\delta y}{\delta x} = 4x + 2\delta x$$
$$\underset{\delta x \to o}{\pounds t}\ \frac{\delta y}{\delta x} = \frac{dy}{dx} = 4x \text{ or } 2(2x)$$

We see that the gradient at any point on this curve $y = 2x^2 + 3$ is the same as the gradient at corresponding points on the curve $y = 2x^2$. Thus the added constant has no effect on the gradient of a curve of similar form. This is clearly borne out by the graphical illustration supplied. In

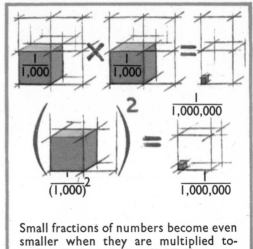

Small fractions of numbers become even smaller when they are multiplied together. So $\delta x \times \delta x$ (i.e. $(\delta x)^2$) disappears from equations in calculus.

order to short circuit this circuitous approach to finding gradients to curves at any point on them, the rule of thumb method is used in practice.

The rule of thumb is stated as follows:

If $y = x^n$ where *n* is any number, positive, negative or fractional, then $\frac{dy}{dx}$ is obtained by multiplying the variable *x* by its index (*n*) and reducing it by one to obtain the value of its new index.

	$y =$	x^2	x^3	x^4	$x^5 \ldots$	$\ldots x^n$
	$\frac{dy}{dx} =$	$2x$	$3x^2$	$4x^3$	$5x^4$	nx^{n-1}
Multiplied constant	$y =$	$2x^2$	$3x^3$	$8x^4$	$10x^5$	ax^n
	$\frac{dy}{dx} =$	$2(2x)$	$3(3x^2)$	$8(4x^3)$	$10(5x^4)$	$a(nx^{n-1})$
Added constant	$y =$	$2x^2 + 2$	$3x^3 + 4$	$8x^4 + 9$	$10x^5 + 15$	$ax^n + K$
	$\frac{dy}{dx} =$	$2(2x)$	$3(3x^2)$	$8(4x^3)$	$10(5x^4)$	$a(nx^{n-1})$

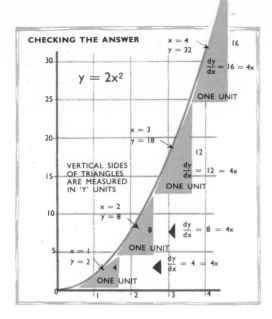

Answers derived from first principles are best checked to make sure that they make sense. The answer for $y = 2x^2$ can be checked by drawing a graph of $y = 2x^2$.

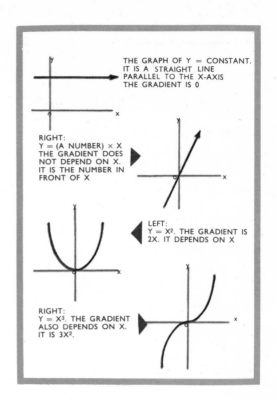

CHAPTER THIRTY-ONE

Maxima and Minima

THE peak of a mountain is the point of maximum height. The climber struggles up a steep gradient to reach the peak, and has to go down a steep gradient to get down again. He can get his breath back at the top because the mountain does not slope there. Its gradient is *zero*.

The gradient of any sloping line is the rate of change of height with horizontal distance. When the line is drawn on a piece of graph paper, the gradient can easily be found with the aid of a ruler. The ruler is moved so that it just touches the curve at the point where its gradient is to be measured. Then a right angled triangle is drawn, with its sloping side a line drawn along the ruler. The

gradient is the length of the vertical side divided by the length of the horizontal side.

At a maximum on a graph, no matter how long the horizontal line is drawn, the length of the vertical side is nil. So the gradient must be nil also..

There may be more than one 'maximum' on the graph, and one peak may be lower than the other. Every peak is called a 'maximum'. A maximum is a point on a curve where the gradient changes from 'up' (a *positive* gradient) on one side of the maximum to a 'down' gradient on the other side.

Between two maxima, the curve usually dips to the bottom of a valley, a *minimum*, and then rises again. The *minimum*, too, is a point

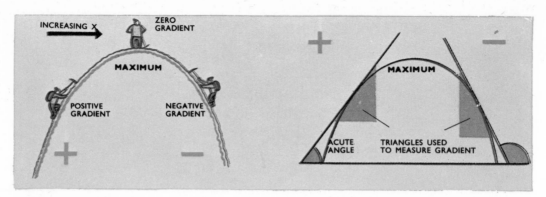

Above: a maximum is a point where the gradient changes from positive to negative. Below: minima occur between two maxima. The gradient changes from negative to positive at the minimum.

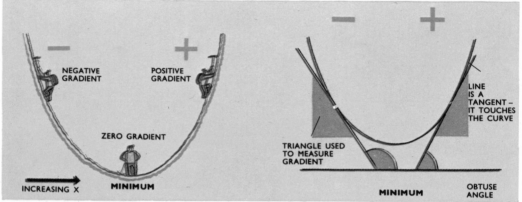

where the gradient is nil.

Maxima and minima occur when the gradient is zero. The gradient is also the quantity found by *differentiation*. The graph shows how y varies when x varies. If y is differentiated with respect to x, the result, the *derivative* written as $\frac{dy}{dx}$, is the gradient. The gradient of a curved line graph varies from point to point along the graph – in other words it depends on 'x'. The derivative is equal to 0 for a maximum or a minimum (i.e. when the gradient is zero). The result of putting $\frac{dy}{dx} = 0$ is an algebraic equation for 'x', giving as its solution the values of x at which the maxima and the minima occur.

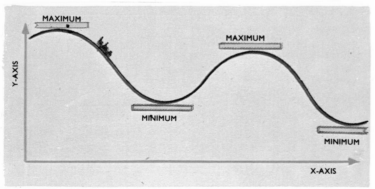

The peaks of the track of a big dipper are maxima and the bottoms of the dips are minima. Maxima and minima are turning points in the slope of the track.

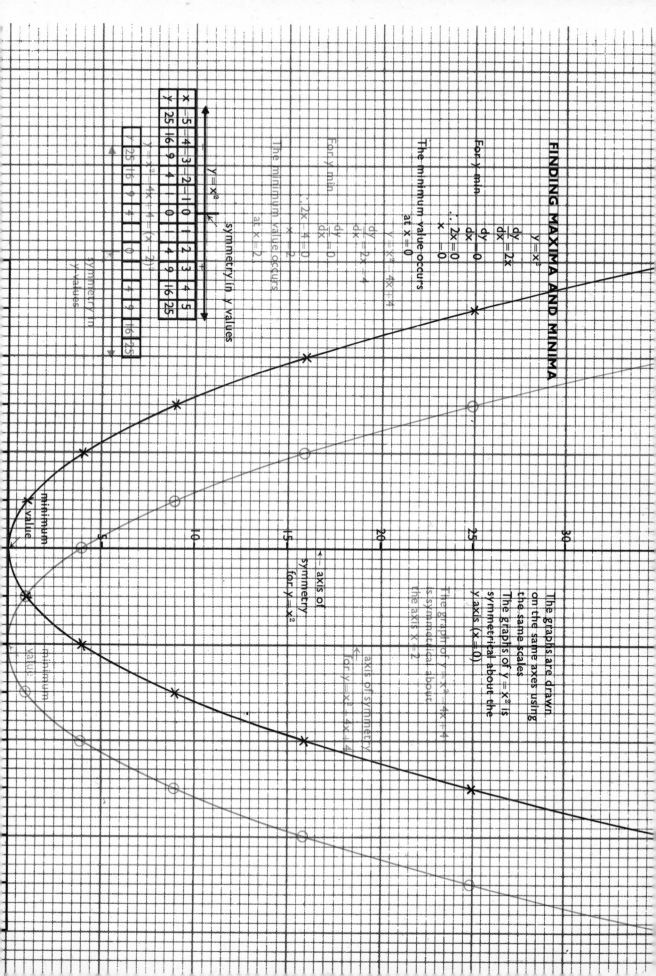

FINDING MAXIMA AND MINIMA

$y = x^2$

$\dfrac{dy}{dx} = 2x$

For y min

$\dfrac{dy}{dx} = 0$

$\therefore 2x = 0$

$x = 0$

The minimum value occurs at $x = 0$

$y = x^2 - 4x + 4$

$\dfrac{dy}{dx} = 2x - 4$

For y min

$\dfrac{dy}{dx} = 0$

$\therefore 2x - 4 = 0$

$x = 2$

The minimum value occurs at $x = 2$

The graphs are drawn on the same axes using the same scales

The graph of $y = x^2$ is symmetrical about the y axis ($x = 0$)

The graph of $y = x^2 - 4x + 4$ is symmetrical about the axis $x = 2$

← axis of symmetry for $y = x^2$

axis of symmetry for $y = x^2 - 4x + 4$ →

$y = x^2$

x	-5	-4	-3	-2	-1	0	1	2	3	4	5
y	25	16	9	4	1	0	1	4	9	16	25

symmetry in y values

$y = x^2 - 4x + 4 = (x - 2)^2$

25	16	9	4	1	0	1	4	9	16	25

symmetry in y values

minimum value

minimum value

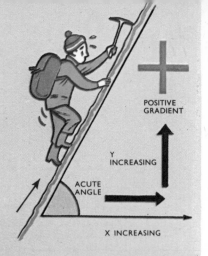

POSITIVE GRADIENT

Y INCREASING

ACUTE ANGLE

X INCREASING

An upward slope makes an acute angle with the direction of increasing x.

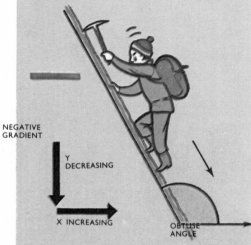

NEGATIVE GRADIENT

Y DECREASING

X INCREASING

OBTUSE ANGLE

A downward slope makes an obtuse angle with the direction of increasing x.

The line touching a curve at its maximum or minimum never meets the horizontal x — axis.

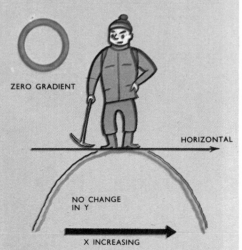

ZERO GRADIENT

HORIZONTAL

NO CHANGE IN Y

X INCREASING

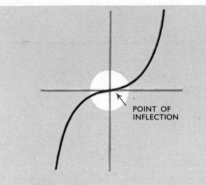

POINT OF INFLECTION

Points of Inflection

Maxima and minima are points on a graph where the curve neither rises nor falls — it stays momentarily steady. The gradient is 0. However, it does not follow that every time the gradient is 0, the point must be a maximum or a minimum. It can be just a lull in a smooth rise or fall — called a *point of inflection*.

FINDING MAXIMA AND MINIMA

If you were made the offer that you could take as much land as you could enclose inside a fixed perimeter you would naturally wish to claim the greatest area of land, especially if you have to pay the present-day phenomenally high prices for the purchase. You would begin to think in terms of squares, rectangles, hexagons, octagons, or even ellipses and circles. Your final choice may or may not have been the correct one if you had resorted to intelligent guesswork. But there is only one way of knowing for certain that you have made the correct choice, and that is by a mathematical calculation. Simple elementary calculations would reveal much more information than just a haphazard and cursory look at the problem. With an eye to symmetry we

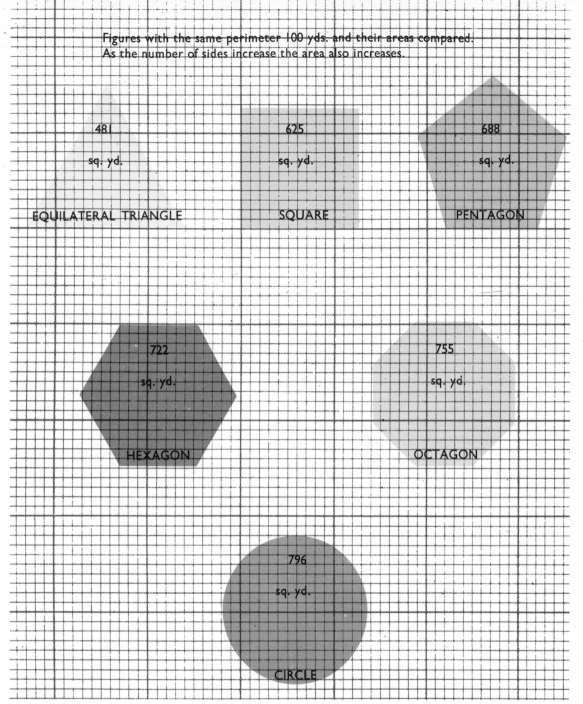

Figures with the same perimeter 100 yds. and their areas compared.
As the number of sides increase the area also increases.

481 sq. yd.
EQUILATERAL TRIANGLE

625 sq. yd.
SQUARE

688 sq. yd.
PENTAGON

722 sq. yd.
HEXAGON

755 sq. yd.
OCTAGON

796 sq. yd.
CIRCLE

draw figures having 3, 4, 5, 6, 8 sides and by simple calculations discover that the greater the number of sides the figure has, the larger the area enclosed for any given perimeter.

Let us for argument's sake take the figure 100 yd. as the constant perimeter. This would give an area of 481 sq. yd. for the *triangle*, 625 sq. yd. for the *square*, 688 sq. yd. for the *pentagon*, 721·6 sq. yd. for the *hexagon*, 795·7 sq. yd. for the *circle*, which is regarded as a figure with an infinite number of sides.

Suppose instead of the original problem the land could be claimed from a base line as one boundary and the shape had to be rectangular. Now we are in a dilemma because a whole lot of rectangles can be drawn having

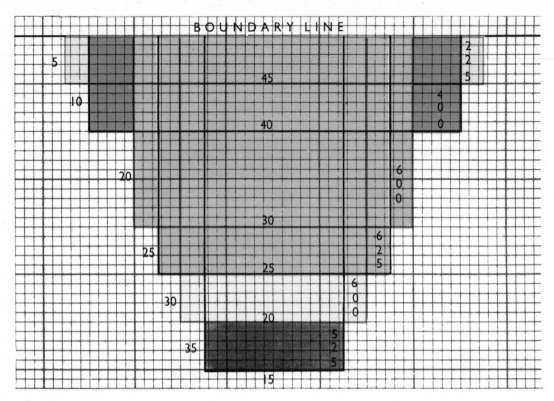

the same perimeter but different areas. By experiment we find that the nearer the values of the sides, the larger the area until when the sides become equal the area is greatest. The Calculus approach for the same number 100 would be as follows:

$$A = l \times b$$

but

$$b = \frac{100 - 2l}{2}$$

∴ $b = 50 - l$

∴ $A = l(50 - l)$

$$A = 50l - l^2$$

$$\frac{dA}{dl} = 50 - 2l$$

For the area to be a maximum

$$\frac{dA}{dl} = 0$$

∴ $50 - 2l = 0$

$$l = 25$$

$$b = 25$$

∴ $A = 25 \times 25$

$$= 625 \text{ sq. yd.}$$

This result proves conclusively that the square has the largest area of all rectangles for a fixed perimeter. Architects use this form of calculation when designing windows which will allow most light through with a fixed perimeter for an opening of given shape. Builders use the same form of calculation when considering the strength of beams used in house construction, for given cross-section. These, and a host of similar problems, can thus be correctly estimated, resulting in efficiency and expertise in industrial development.

Example 1

The stiffness of a beam is given by the formula $S = kwh^3$ where k is a constant, w is the width and h is the depth of the beam. This beam is cut from a cylindrical log of diameter 12″. Find the dimensions of the stiffest beam that can be cut from this log.

Simple Algebraic part:

$$S = Kwh^3$$

By Pythagoras' theorem

$$w^2 + h^2 = 12^2$$
$$w^2 = 12^2 - h^2$$
$$w = (12^2 - h^2)^{\frac{1}{2}}$$
$$\therefore \quad S = Kh^3(12^2 - h^2)^{\frac{1}{2}}$$

The Calculus part:

$$\text{For} \quad S_{max} \frac{dS}{dh} = 0$$

Differentiating and equating to zero we have

$$\frac{dS}{dh} = K[(12^2 - h^2)^{\frac{1}{2}} \times 3h^2$$
$$+ (-2h)(12^2 - h^2)^{-\frac{1}{2}} . \tfrac{1}{2}] \times h^3 = 0.$$

Multiplying through by $(12^2 - h^2)^{+\frac{1}{2}}$ and dividing by K we have

$$(12^2 - h^2) . 3h^2 - h^4 = 0$$

Dividing through by h^2, gives

$$h = 0$$

and

$$3(144 - h^2) = h^2$$
$$4h^2 = 3 \times 144$$
$$h^2 = 3 \times 36$$
$$h = ^{\pm} 6\sqrt{3}$$
$$w^2 = 144 - 108 = 36$$

and

$$w = ^{\pm} 6$$

This gives the height of the beam to be $6\sqrt{3}''$ and its width $6''$.

The method of differentiating is the method of differentiating product functions and is beyond the scope of this book.

Example 2

A window consists of a semi-circle surmounting a rectangle. The diameter of the semi-circle is the same as the width of the rectangle. If the perimeter of the window is 12 ft. what is its width so that it allows the maximum light through?

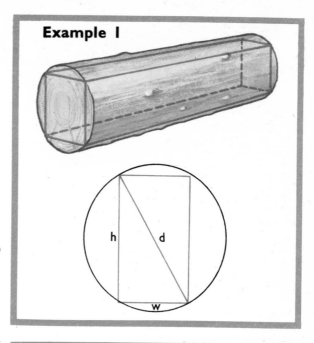

Example 1

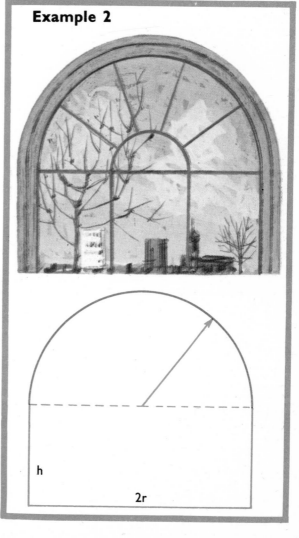

Example 2

Simple Algebraic part:

Perimeter
$$P = \pi r + 2r + 2h = 12$$
$$2h = 12 - \pi r - 2r$$
$$h = 6 - r - \frac{\pi r}{2}.$$

$$\text{Area } A = \frac{\pi r^2}{2} + 2rh$$
$$= \frac{\pi r^2}{2} + 2r\left(6 - r - \frac{\pi r}{2}\right)$$
$$= \frac{\pi r^2}{2} + 12r - 2r^2 - \pi r^2$$
$$= 12r - 2r^2 - \frac{\pi r^2}{2}$$

The Calculus part:

$$\text{For } A_{max} \quad \frac{dA}{dr} = 0$$

Differentiating and equating to zero we have

$$\frac{dA}{dr} = 12 - 4r - \pi r = 0$$
$$\therefore \qquad 4r + \pi r = 12$$
$$r(4 + \pi) = 12$$
$$r = \frac{12}{(4 + \pi)}$$

$$\text{Width} = 2r = \frac{24}{4 + \pi} = 3\cdot362 \text{ ft.}$$

Appendix

PERMUTATIONS AND COMBINATIONS

A PERMUTATION is a way of arranging a number of different things. If there are 8 people waiting to fill 8 seats around a table, then each way of arranging them is called a *permutation*. The number of different permutations is often fantastically large. There are in fact 40,320 ways of arranging 8 people in 8 places around a rectangular table. This number can be calculated quite easily.

At the start, there are 8 empty seats and 8 occupants for them. So there are 8 different ways of filling the first seat alone. When the first seat is filled 7 occupants are left. As there were 8 different ways of filling the first seat, there are now 7 different ways of filling the second seat. For each one of the 8 possibilities for the first seat, there are 7 possibilities for the second seat. So the number of ways of filling the first two seats is

$$8 \times 7 = 56.$$

Only 6 people remain to fill the remaining 6 seats. The third seat can be filled by any one of these, which means that there are 6 ways of filling it. The total number of ways of filling the first three seats is therefore

$$8 \times 7 \times 6 = 336.$$

The number of ways
of filling 4 places is $8 \times 7 \times 6 \times 5$ (= 1,680)
of filling 5 places is $8 \times 7 \times 6 \times 5 \times 4$ (= 6,720)
of filling 6 places is $8 \times 7 \times 6 \times 5 \times 4 \times 3$ (= 20,160)
of filling 7 places is $8 \times 7 \times 6 \times 5 \times 4 \times 3 \times 2$ (= 40,320)
of filling 8 places is $8 \times 7 \times 6 \times 5 \times 4 \times 3 \times 2 \times 1$ (= 40,320)
which makes a grand total of 40,320 different ways.

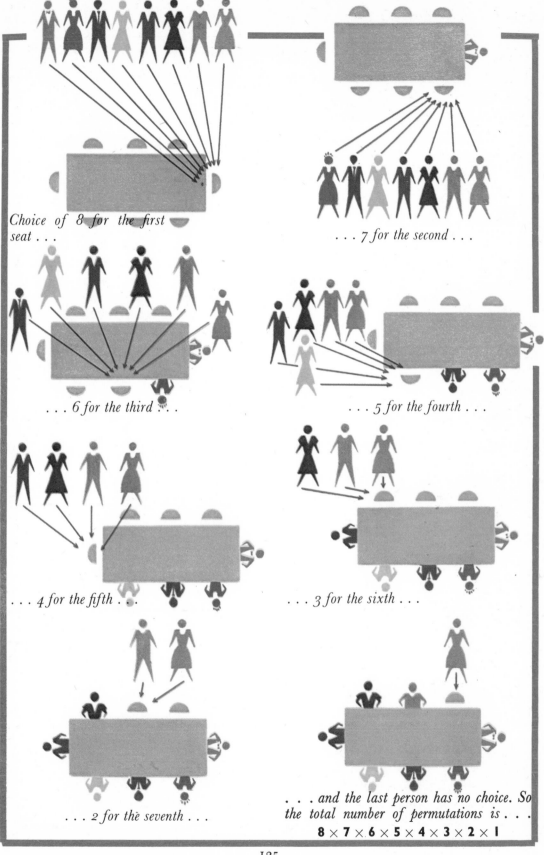

Choice of 8 for the first seat . . .

. . . 7 for the second . . .

. . . 6 for the third . . .

. . . 5 for the fourth . . .

. . . 4 for the fifth . . .

. . . 3 for the sixth . . .

. . . 2 for the seventh . . .

. . . and the last person has no choice. So the total number of permutations is . . .

8 × 7 × 6 × 5 × 4 × 3 × 2 × 1

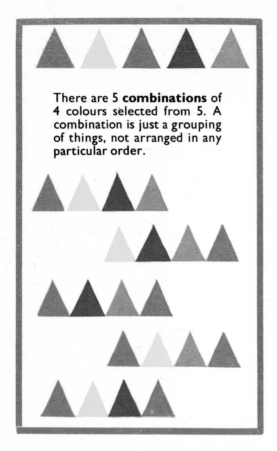

There are 5 **combinations** of 4 colours selected from 5. A combination is just a grouping of things, not arranged in any particular order.

Similarly, there are 5 possibilities for the fourth seat, 4 for the fifth, 3 for the sixth, 2 for the seventh, and the last remaining person automatically fills the eighth place.

The number
$8 \times 7 \times 6 \times 5 \times 4 \times 3 \times 2 \times 1$
is given the name *factorial* 8 (symbol 8!).

The number of permutations can be worked out in a similar way if there are more occupants than seats, or more seats than occupants. When 8 people contend for only 4 seats, the total number of ways of filling the seats is $8 \times 7 \times 6 \times 5$; that is, the first *4* factors of *factorial* 8. If only 4 people are available for 8 seats, the number of permutations is exactly

the same. The first person has the choice of 8 seats, the second of 7, and so on. So the number of permutations is $8 \times 7 \times 6 \times 5$, or 1,680.

Permutations are ways of arranging things in a definite order. People sitting around a table are sitting in a definite order, so the ways of arranging them are permutations.

Often confused with permutations are *combinations*, where the order in which the things are arranged is not considered at all. When there are 8 people, but only 4 seats, then there are $8 \times 7 \times 6 \times 5$ ways of arranging them in order (permutations). But if the seating arrangement is unimportant, and we simply want to know the possible groups of 4 people selected from the 8, to sit anywhere around the table, then we are dealing with *combinations*.

While there are 1,680 permutations of 4 people chosen from 8, there are only 70 *combinations*. The number is smaller because the order is not considered. The best way of proving that there are 70 combinations is to find out what must be done to the number of combinations to make it equal to the number of permutations.

For each one of the combinations (i.e. for each set of four people) there are $4 \times 3 \times 2 \times 1$ ways of arranging them in order (i.e. 24 permutations). So for all the combinations, the number of permutations is equal to the number of combinations $\times 4 \times 3 \times 2 \times 1$.

So the number of combinations is

the $\dfrac{\text{number of permutations}}{4 \times 3 \times 2 \times 1}$

i.e. $\dfrac{1,680}{4 \times 3 \times 2 \times 1}$

or 70.

Index

DATE DUE

GAYLORD			PRINTED IN U.S A.